Off Guard

"Woody Webster. You are the most frustrating person in the world," yelled Kim, charging at him. He dodged lightly out of her way, and playfully rumpled her hair as he did. Kim charged again. This time he ran behind a large pine tree. Kim rushed around one side and then the other, but each time he just escaped her grasp. Finally she caught him off guard and grabbed his shirt sleeve. They spun around and around then fell to the ground, Kim landing on top of Woody. Her face was inches from his. His eyes were shiny and devilish-looking. That sweet, funny smile, which had dominated her thoughts for so many hours, was now miraculously close. Before she even thought about the consequences, Kim felt herself leaning toward Woody. Their mouths met and his lips were as warm and tender as she had imagined.

Books from Scholastic
in the Couples series:

COUPLES

CRAZY LOVE

M.E. Cooper

SCHOLASTIC INC.
New York Toronto London Auckland Sydney

ISBN 0-590-33395-X

Copyright © 1985 by Cloverdale Press.
All rights reserved. Published by Scholastic Inc.

12 11 10 9 8 7 6 5 4 3 2 1   11   5 6 7 8 9 /8 0/9

Printed in the U.S.A.   06

CRAZY LOVE

Chapter
1

Phoebe stared out the window at the rain-drenched world. At close focus the wire mesh in the reinforced glass turned her view into a strange, surreal puzzle of regular, hexagonal shapes. But when she looked beyond this, letting the window fade away, the scene was soft and dreamlike, washed in gray. The trees were no longer rooted to the ground but floated magically between heaven and earth. The hill beyond the track began but never ended.

As she leaned against the gym door waiting to rotate into a volleyball game, Phoebe didn't hear the noise all around her — the loud mumble of students talking at once, the crashing of feet up and down the bleachers, the occasional plea from the gym teacher to keep it down. The rain had kept seventh period physical education classes inside for the day, and the gym was pulsing with enough pent-up energy to light the town of Rose Hill for a year or two. But Phoebe was barely aware of it. She was lost in the beauty of the soft gray world outside.

"Pheeberooni!"

The familiar voice called Phoebe to attention. Slowly the world outside returned to reality — the soaking, wet grounds of Kennedy High tucked away in the suburban hills of Maryland.

"Hi ya, Pheeb, what's cooking?" asked Woody, bouncing up to her side in his regulation Kennedy gymsuit, T-shirt, and his usual high-topped sneakers. "You look like you've taken up meditation." He followed Phoebe's stare out the window. "Ugh, what a miserable day, huh?"

"Oh, I don't know," said Phoebe dreamily. "I was just thinking it was kind of neat."

"Neat if you have webbed feet, or an ark to launch," joked Woody, shaking his mop of curls. His brown eyes twinkled. "Me, I'm into sunshine and warm sand. Rio de Janeiro sounds good to me right now. What you say? Want to grab the last flight out of Dulles tonight to the sunny south?"

Phoebe laughed. "I'd love to, Woody, but I'm afraid the only place my parents are letting me go these days is to the bathroom and back."

"Are you still grounded?" asked Woody in surprise.

"For two more weeks." Phoebe sighed. "Might as well be a zillion years. It sure feels that long. Do you know how boring one room can get after a while?"

"You mean they've actually got you in solitary confinement?" said Woody dramatically. "Have they put you on bread and water yet?"

Phoebe giggled. "Oh, Woody. Who gave you permission to put me in a good mood?"

"Well, I must admit you looked like you could use a little cheering up the way you were huddled next to the door over here. Have you known each other long?"

"For years," Phoebe shot back, tossing her thick red braid over her shoulder. "We were just discussing if we should go steady. I'm game; it all hinges on the door."

"That's good, Pheeb, very good indeed. Maybe I should get you up on the stage to do a comedy routine for my next follies."

A pain stabbed Phoebe's heart. She didn't want to be reminded of the follies, of that magical few weeks she still hadn't figured out yet. Griffin and she had sung in Woody's show, they had fallen in love — Phoebe's life had reached a new high. Then Griffin had gone to New York, and abruptly disappeared. Their final phone conversation had been incomprehensible. He said he had decided she shouldn't come to New York for the visit they had planned. Then he cut her off completely. No more calls. No more letters. If she could find it within herself to hate him, maybe she could get on with her own life. But she loved Griffin, loved him with an intensity that almost frightened her. Her relationship with Brad had been secure, but her feelings for Griffin crackled with electricity. Griffin made her feel alive.

"Am I boring you, Pheeb?" asked Woody eventually. "You really are off in the ozone today."

"I'm sorry, Woody," said Phoebe. "It must be the weather. It sort of crowds all my thoughts into my head at once."

"Need anyone to handle valet parking?" he joked. "Sounds kind of chaotic in there."

Phoebe smiled warmly at her old friend. They'd known each other since sixth grade and even though she knew Woody would prefer their relationship to be more than just platonic, their friendship was solid.

"How's your car?" asked Phoebe, trying to keep herself from spacing out again.

"Ah, yes . . . my car . . . what's left of my car, you mean. You and that tree obviously had a very close relationship. They're still picking bark out of the fender."

"Woody, don't tease," groaned Phoebe. She'd been driving Woody's Volvo back from her parents' cabin after picking up Sasha and her new boyfriend Wes. Phoebe's parents had lent the cabin to someone else for the day without telling her, so she had to rescue her friends before her parents found out Phoebe had given them permission to use it. "You know how sick I feel about that. Are they going to be able to repair it completely? I mean, so it looks exactly the same?"

"It's going to be better than ever. They're even throwing in a new paint job: cherry red. Am I going to be cool, or what? The girls are going to be crawling all over me."

"They would, if you'd stand still long enough." Phoebe laughed. Phoebe knew that Woody was every girl's friend; the first person a girl turned to when she had boy troubles; the first person invited to all the parties. But Woody never had a girl friend. He was certainly attractive in a warm, cuddly, Groucho Marx sort of way. Everyone trusted him.

Phoebe's gaze wandered around the crowded gym. "Excuse me, everyone. Hey, hold it up a minute, you clowns," demanded Mr. Mattson, the gym teacher, clapping his hands sharply. "While we're all sitting in here waiting for the school to float away," continued Mr. Mattson, "Kimberly Barrie would like to make an announcement. Let's give her our attention."

Phoebe and Woody settled down on the crowded bleachers. Kim bounced to the middle of the gym, her athletic stride exuding confidence and determination. Several boys whistled from the back of the bleachers, but Kim didn't stop. Digging down into her baggy linen trousers, she pulled her glasses out and perched them on the end of her nose. Her T-shirt had a picture of Margaret Thatcher, the prime minister of Great Britain, on it. Underneath was written: BUT CAN SHE TYPE?

Phoebe smiled. Kim had only been at Kennedy High for a few months, but already she'd made her mark. She was a doer. People were always trying to draft her for their committees, because if Kimberly Barrie were working for a cause, things got done — fast. And Phoebe had heard that Kim, who helped run her mother's catering business, was a top-notch cook.

Phoebe wished she'd had the opportunity to get to know Kim better, but almost since Kim's arrival at Kennedy, she had been grounded. Every day she went straight home to tackle the list of projects her parents had assigned her to earn back the money for the repairs to Woody's car. Phoebe was sick of cleaning windows and washing floors.

"Hi, everyone," began Kim. "Nice day for ducks, huh?"

A loud groan issued forth. Kim smiled up at the crowd.

"Okay, at least I got your attention. Now I want your bodies."

"All right!" shouted the boys in the back.

Woody sat up straight, his whole attention focused on the small girl in the middle of the gym.

"Yes, your bodies," continued Kim. "Especially your legs. As you know, or may not know — officials don't usually like to publicize such things — the girls' track team at Kennedy High isn't as well funded as the boys' team. That means the girls may be jogging to about half their meets, unless we come up with some extra bucks. The girls' team had an 8-2 season last year, so I think they deserve our support, don't you?"

Shouts of approval reverberated through the gym, Woody's leading the pack.

"Okay. Great. Thank you. What we're proposing is a run-a-thon. Three weeks from Saturday. That means all you closet runners have three weeks to get pledges from area stores and merchants. Your parents. Your dog and cat. The goldfish next door. Whoever. We need every penny we can get. Why not say a quarter for every quarter mile you run? That has a nice ring

6

to it. Then after you've run, you're responsible for collecting the pledges."

Kim peered over the top of her glasses. "Any questions about that part?"

"No," roared back the answer.

"Great. You can get pledge forms from me or any member of the girls' track team, so let's get moving. What do you say?"

Woody leapt to his feet, shouting and stomping his approval. Phoebe clapped until her hands were red. It was a great speech. And if it hadn't been raining, she felt sure everyone in the gym would have poured out onto the track right then.

Mr. Mattson dismissed the class to change. After she had put on her jeans and stowed her gymsuit, Phoebe returned to the bleachers to meet Woody.

"Whew, she's something!" said Woody, picking up his books. "Really something."

Phoebe followed Woody's intent gaze across the gym. There was a new tone in his voice. He was staring at Kim as he struggled to put on his cycling poncho. It was backwards.

"Want a ride home, Woody?" she asked, watching him struggle.

"Ride! You mean after what you did you still have a car?"

"You know parents. There's no logic," said Phoebe, heading for the exit. "My mother figures if she gives me the car, then I can do all her errands for her after school."

"That sounds delightfully boring," said Woody.

"Well, when you've been grounded for as long as I have, picking up a half pound of coffee can

7

be positively fascinating," said Phoebe. "Just to stand there watching it being ground up to medium fine for electric perk can be the highlight of my week."

Woody shook his head. "Poor old Phoebe. You've finally gone over the edge. I didn't expect it to happen so soon."

Phoebe laughed.

"I wish your parents didn't take this thing with the car so seriously," said Woody. "After all, it's *my* car that got trashed, and I'm certainly not going to pieces over it. I think a couple of months in Outer Mongolia would have been sufficient punishment."

"At least Outer Mongolia would be a change of pace," agreed Phoebe. "Did you know that there are one thousand three hundred twenty-eight bunches of flowers on the wallpaper in my room, four hundred thirty-two stripes on my bedspread, and a total of nine hundred eighteen different English words on the *Annie* soundtrack?"

"Actually, Phoebe, I did know all that," deadpanned Woody, snapping his suspenders. "Except I believe *Annie* has nine hundred nineteen words. I'd be happy to help you do a recount."

"Aaaarrrrrgh . . . you can be the most infuriating person in the world," said Phoebe, swinging her backpack at him playfully. "If I ever ask you for your car again, please deny you even know me. Okay?"

"And if you just decide to take it like you did on that fateful day, what then?"

"Don't remind me," groaned Phoebe, pulling

her keys out of the side pocket of her coat as they approached the car.

"Let's go check my bike. I want to be sure it's locked up for the night," said Woody, steering her over to the rack of bicycles by the flagpole.

"But you never lock your bike," protested Phoebe. "You told me you keep hoping someone will steal it, so you'll have an excuse to get a new one."

"Today I'm going to lock it," said Woody emphatically.

Phoebe looked over at the bikes and immediately realized that Woody had an ulterior motive. Kim was leaning over her bike, fiddling with her lock. Phoebe was surprised to feel a twinge of jealousy. She had always encouraged Woody to find a girl friend, but so far he hadn't; she'd always been number one with him. Until that very moment she hadn't realized how secure Woody's faithful friendship made her feel.

"Hi, Kim," sang out Woody. "That was one inspired speech you gave today. Great job."

Kim looked up, startled, then her face turned pink when she spotted Woody. "Oh hi, Woody, Phoebe. Thanks. I'm a desperate woman. The girls' team really is low on funds."

"I didn't know you were on the track team. What do you run? The mile dash? The two-mile?"

Phoebe almost burst out laughing. Woody didn't know a thing about track. He prided himself on avoiding anything even slightly athletic, although the way he rode his bike convinced Phoebe that he really did care about keeping in shape. He was tall and wiry, the perfect build for

9

a high jumper, but even the suggestion brought moans and groans of protest.

"I don't run anything, actually," replied Kim. "But it makes me angry that the boys are always getting first dibs on everything. The girls' teams work just as hard as they do. And they have a better record. So I believe they deserve all the help they can get."

Phoebe could see that Woody was slightly taken aback by the force of this speech, but he smiled down at Kim.

"I totally agree. Good for you," he said. His smile widened. "Keep up the good work."

"Kim, would you like a ride home?" asked Phoebe. The rain was coming down harder, splashing noisily in the puddles across the parking lot.

"Oh no, thanks anyway," said Kim, her green eyes shining. "I love riding in the rain."

"You sure?" repeated Phoebe. "It wouldn't be any trouble." She would have loved the opportunity to talk with Kim. Kim had an open, direct style that Phoebe admired.

"Positive," replied Kim, swinging her backpack onto her back. "I've been looking forward to getting out in this all day. Bye now."

Phoebe and Woody watched Kim disappear into the fog, then turned back to the big, fat station wagon that would take them home. The car seemed terribly normal and boring to Phoebe — there was Kim, off on an adventure, weaving her way in and out of the fog, feeling the rain splatter against her face. She and Woody were going to encase themselves in a stuffy metal box, insulated from the elements, and all those wonderful sensations.

Phoebe remembered her first walk in the rain with Griffin. Like Kim, he loved it; he'd thrown his head back and let the gentle drops tap-dance on his face. Phoebe thought he was insane at first; but when he finally talked her into trying it, she'd loved it, too. She had regretted all the times she'd cursed the rain.

Slowly Phoebe unlocked the car and got in. All those wonderful things Griffin had taught her seemed to be slipping away. If only she knew where he was, if she could imagine him somewhere, or at least know he was all right. But Woody had just come back from New York, where he spent a couple of days looking for Griffin. Griffin had told Phoebe that he was cast in a Broadway show, but no one connected with the show had heard of him. It was like an episode of *The Twilight Zone*.

Phoebe could feel herself begin to crumble inside. Immediately she tried to think of something else. She'd gone over the same questions again and again: Where was he? Why had he lied to her about getting that part in the play? Why had he invited her to New York, then told her not to come? Why couldn't he explain his change of heart? Not knowing what was going on made Phoebe feel like she was spinning her wheels, stuck in place, unable to go forward.

"What do you think of her, Pheeb?" asked Woody.

"Who?" replied Phoebe, her mind still miles away, searching for Griffin.

"Kim, dummy."

"She seems like a really neat person. I wish I had half her drive. I mean, she acts as though she knows where she's going in life. I bet she's the kind of person who'll be the first woman president someday."

"Yeah . . . I think she's neat, too."

"You mean 'neat' as in you'd-like-to-date-her neat?" asked Phoebe, giving him a smile.

"Oh, no . . . no, no, no" said Woody quickly. "Nothing like that. Besides, she already has a boyfriend."

"Who?" asked Phoebe in surprise. She'd never seen Kim with anyone at Kennedy, and they passed each other in the halls several times a day.

"Some guy back in Pittsburgh," said Woody. "Where she lived before she moved to Rose Hill. They're pretty tight."

"Keeping a long-distance romance going isn't easy," said Phoebe. "Maybe she'll drop him or it'll just fizzle out of its own accord — "

"Maybe it will, maybe it won't," broke in Woody. "But I can tell you one thing: I'm not going to sit around and wait for something to happen. Do you realize I've spent my entire dating life getting interested in girls who already have other boyfriends? Don't you think Dr. Freud would find that kind of peculiar?"

Phoebe laughed. "Freud! If he ever met you he'd have to invent a whole new branch of psychology. Yes, I think he'd find you *very* interesting."

"And I call you a friend," joked Woody. "Makes me wonder who I'd pick for an enemy.

Besides, even if she does break up with that jerk, why should I think she would turn around and fall into my arms? She'd probably just come and cry on my shoulder and then fall for some hunk. That's the way it's always been. No, I've had it with girls who have boyfriends. It just doesn't pay."

For a moment Phoebe didn't know what to say. In some ways what Woody was saying was true. After all, wasn't she living proof? When she'd broken up with Brad because of Griffin she had known Woody was interested in her, but she left him standing in the wings. Maybe he should have felt complimented that all the girls thought of him as their friend. Not getting involved with anyone sure kept his life simple. But he was ready for something more — Phoebe could feel it. She'd sensed it for some time. Woody wanted to be special to someone.

"Well, all out for the Webster residence," sang out Phoebe. "Be sure to check the overhead rack for your personal belongings, and have a nice day."

"Thanks a lot for the ride, Pheeb," said Woody. "Maybe I can do the same for you one day."

"Hopefully after your car's fixed or your bike's stolen," retorted Phoebe with a laugh.

Woody was about to slam the door when Phoebe grabbed his arm.

"Woody," she said softly.

"Uh, oh," said Woody, rolling his eyes. "I know that tone of voice. What do you want? You know I'm such a sucker I'll give it to you. Anything."

13

"Remember the agent that called Griffin? Didn't you say he was a friend of your mother's?"

"Well, not a close friend, but she had some dealings with him through Arena Stage." Woody's mother was the manager of this small, but prestigious theater in Washington, and she knew a lot of people from the New York theatrical world. Woody, who ran most of the stage productions at Kennedy, was following his mother's career.

"Do you think you could get me his name and phone number? I'm getting really worried that something terrible might have happened to Griffin. It's just not like him to act like he did on the phone the last time we talked — all uptight and impatient. I've got to find out what's going on. I'm going nuts not knowing."

"Pheeb, of course I'll try to find out what I can for you. But don't you think you're getting a little too obsessed about all this? Maybe the guy just wanted to break up and didn't know how to come right out and say it."

Phoebe felt tears sting her eyes. She'd wondered the same thing many times, but kept pushing it to the back of her mind. She couldn't bring herself to believe the worst yet. Being with Griffin had given her so much strength; she needed his support. They were right for each other — she knew it.

"Maybe he does," she said. "But why couldn't he just tell me? At least then I'd be sure of what's going on."

"You could be headed for a lot of pain, my friend," Woody said, gently taking her hand.

Phoebe turned her head so Woody wouldn't

see the tears start down her cheeks.

"I know . . . I know, but I've got to get some answers."

"Okay. I'll check with my mom tonight and see what she can come up with. I'm sure we can get to the bottom of this." He squeezed her hand.

Phoebe smiled warmly through her tears. "Thank you, Woody. I don't know what I'd do without you."

"That's what all you girls say," he joked. "You don't know what to do with me, but you can't do without me. I wonder if Robert Redford has all these problems!"

Phoebe laughed. It was impossible to be down around Woody. "You clown. See you tomorrow."

Driving home Phoebe began to imagine that every dark shape looming up in the thick fog was Griffin. He'd come back. No . . . he'd never gone away, the whole New York thing was a nightmare that had never happened. He was waiting for her on the next street, down the next block, around that far corner. She could see his gray-blue eyes searching her face as they had so many times; she could feel his arms around her, strong and warm and caring. She could feel the energy flowing from his body to hers.

A sob rose in Phoebe's throat. Where was he? Maybe he was in some sort of terrible trouble. Sick. Dying. Or maybe Woody was right: Maybe she was just a brief fling in his life — like a curtain that had gone up and then just as quickly been brought down again, an interlude between major productions. Phoebe felt as though she would burst with the pain of not knowing.

Chapter
2

Kim felt relieved to get away from Woody and Phoebe, to escape into the peaceful quiet of the fog. For some reason she felt disoriented and out of control, a condition that was totally out of character for her. Kim knew that her ideas might strike the other kids as kind of radical — but she had a strong sense of what she wanted in life, and went after her goals in a straightforward way.

Maybe she had gotten to be that way because she had had to move so much, she mused as she slipped into an easy, steady cycling motion. Her dad's job with the Department of the Interior as an advisor on Indian affairs meant that they had had to change addresses every two years or so. Being the new kid all the time was kind of tough, so she'd developed her own protective shell of confidence that she would slip into as she moved from school to school. Kennedy was her second high school so far. Kennedy had

16

Woody Webster though, and somehow for the first time in a long while, she felt a little uncertain about where she was headed.

But why, Kim wondered as she turned into her driveway and pushed her bike up the steep hill at the end. Ever since she'd met him at Ted Mason's party, she'd been impressed by him. She admired people who knew what they wanted and how to get it, and Woody definitely knew what he was all about. He was so funny and had so much talent, a real individual. She loved being around him, but she was also a little relieved to get away from him. Why was that? Something didn't make sense. Maybe it was just that she missed David. After all, they hadn't seen each other in almost two months, not since she moved from Pittsburgh.

"Hi, Mom," said Kim, slamming the back door, which was swollen by the damp and barely closable. The house was nice and warm, and smelled heavenly. As she walked through the mud room to the kitchen, Kim marveled at the changes her mother had wrought in the old house in such a short time. The kitchen had been her first project, and within a week of their moving in it was gutted. Now, it looked very high-tech, all white and stainless steel, with splashes of color here and there as accents: red-and-white striped towels, a sassy arrangement of red silk flowers in a black vase, and above the sink, a stained-glass window her father had secretly ordered for them. Etched in deep, rich colors were the words "Earthly Delights" — the name of their catering business. Kim loved this room almost as much as her mother did. They spent a lot of time there together as they worked hard to get the business going. Now it was just beginning to get off the ground.

"Hello, dear. Nice day?" Her mother's black hair was sprinkled with flour dust. Her eyes, though dark, sparkled with the same fire that lit Kim's green ones.

"Pretty good. I've decided I like Kennedy. There are a few creeps, but I guess you find them everywhere, huh?"

"Amen," replied her mother, rolling out another ball of dough. "Want to help?"

"What are you making?" asked Kim, sniffing the little rows of completed pastries. "They sure look good."

"A new recipe: crab imperial pasties. Basic pâté brisée filled with crab meat and herbs."

"Hmmmmmm. Sounds delicious. May I have one?"

"Have I ever denied you anything?" Her mother laughed, handing her a warm pastry. "After all, it was you who got me into this mess in the first place."

It was true. The catering service had been Kim's idea. She could tell that her mother had started to feel restless now that her three children were basically grown-up. The two older ones were away at college. For a while after moving to Rose Hill, her mom tried to be a lady of leisure, sticking to a heavy schedule of tennis matches and bridge games. But this frenzy lasted only about a week before she'd started to feel bored and dissatisfied. It was about that time when Kim read an article in *Seventeen* about a mother-daughter catering service. She'd mentioned it to her mom and within the week they were putting it together.

The magazine article featured a service especially for birthday parties, but her mother felt the suburbs of Washington, D.C. had different needs. There was a high percentage of working mothers in the area, so she planned to freeze gourmet meals that these busy women could stack in the freezer to prepare whenever they needed them.

"What can I help you do?" asked Kim, licking her fingers appreciatively. "Looks like you have a big order."

"We do," replied her mother excitedly. "I think it must have been those signs you put up all over the place. Mrs. Fitch. You know Gerald Fitch, the senator? Well, his wife is throwing a huge tea party this weekend."

"Tea and crab pasties?!" broke in Kim. "Isn't that kind of a weird combination?"

"Well, I suppose that's because what a tea party means to politicians is cocktails at five," replied her mother. She and Kim broke into giggles.

"I've got one hundred fifty of these things to make. Can you believe it?" her mother asked.

"Whew. In that case, I better take the whole week off from school to help," said Kim, wrapping her favorite apron around her waist. Splashed across the front was: "A WOMAN'S PLACE IS IN THE WHITE HOUSE."

"Nice try, sneaky daughter of mine, but I think I'll be able to manage on my own. After

19

we've made our first million you have my permission to quit school and become a full-time partner."

Kim groaned dramatically and started rolling out the dough. Suddenly she stopped, the rolling pin suspended midair. "Wait a minute, Mom. I won't even be here this weekend to help you. I'm going to Pittsburgh, remember? To see David."

"Goodness, I'd forgotten all about that. It snuck up on me so quickly. Can it really be the eleventh already?"

"It will be on Friday." Kim hesitated. "I can go to Pittsburgh some other time, though. This is our first big break. You're going to need my help. I should be here."

"Don't be silly, dear," said her mother. "I can manage just fine on my own. Besides, I know how much this trip means to you."

"Well . . . yes, I guess so," replied Kim, surprised at how unenthusiastic she really felt about it. But, after all, she and her mom had put a lot of energy into launching the catering business. "I just think it's equally important to be here when the business needs me, too."

Mrs. Barrie looked at her daughter with genuine surprise. "Did something go wrong between you and David?"

"No, Mom, not at all. It's just that I've got things to do, and David has things to do, and we don't have to do everything together. Earthly Delights is very important to me. I want to see it really take off. We deserve it."

"I guess I'm just old-fashioned," said her

mother, shaking her head. "I still believe the man comes first."

"I know you do, Mom. But I've watched you remold your whole life every two years. Just because Dad gets transferred, you always have to stop whatever you're doing and follow him," explained Kim.

"I know, dear, but I love your father. What's important to him is important to me. I've never thought of myself as being particularly self-sacrificing."

"I know you haven't. You've been wonderful about all the changes we've had to make. But remember when you were working as a paralegal in Wyoming?"

"Ummm," said her mother dreamily. "I really enjoyed that work."

"Well, if we'd stayed there, you'd probably be a lawyer by now," said Kim. "But Dad's career took a step up, so yours had to take a step down. That's so unfair! I've decided I'm never going to let myself get in that kind of situation. My husband is going to have to think about my career, too, and maybe not get to climb his own ladder as fast as he might like to."

"You're absolutely right, of course," replied her mother. "But don't you think that's going to complicate your life a lot?"

"Maybe, but I'd rather have a complicated life than an unexciting one," said Kim, then added, "I'm sorry Mom. I don't mean that your life has been unexciting."

"I know you don't, dear. In many ways I envy

your generation. You have so many choices that we didn't have, but at the same time I feel a bit sorry for you, too. All those choices are going to give you a lot of headaches that I didn't have to face in my time. Like what career to go into. Killing yourself to get into the best college so that you can be ahead of the competition. Whew! I honestly don't know how you cope sometimes. When I grew up, you knew what you were supposed to do: try to be the best wife and mother possible."

Kim smiled and put her arms around her mother. "Mom, you *are* the best."

"There. That's the greatest reward to me. That's all I want right now," said her mother, returning the hug. "Oh, by the way, I forgot to tell you. David called. About half an hour ago."

"Thanks. I guess he'll call back," replied Kim, going back to her dough rolling.

Her mother looked at her curiously. "Are you sure everything's all right with you and David? You don't seem especially excited about him these days."

"I don't know, Mom. I guess I am. I mean, as much as I ever was," said Kim, attacking the dough fiercely. "It's just that our relationship was never, you know, super passionate or anything like that — maybe that's for the best. I've seen so many girls flip out over some guy and lose themselves completely. I guess maybe in the beginning it was like that with David, too, but after awhile the whole thing just seemed kind of pointless." Kim rolled the rubbery dough into a big, crooked circle. "Remember my telling you about Laurie Bennington?"

"You mean the one who gave you the rundown your second day at Kennedy, on what you were supposed to do and how you were supposed to act, so you could make it with 'the crowd'?"

Kim giggled. "You got it. She's the one. Well, she started dating Lars Olsen, the Swedish exchange student, about a month ago, and now you'd think she was a full-blooded Swede. I can't believe it. She practically has a Swedish accent now. She came to school all winter in bulky sweaters with herds of reindeer knitted all over them and these corduroy knickers — like for cross-country skiing. I mean, this is the former Laurie of the eternally-exposed-shoulder-and-thigh style."

"Oh, my," her mother laughed. "I love your description of the sweater. I can just see those poor little reindeer wandering all over her chest like a herd of lost sheep. . . ."

"Honestly, Mom, you wouldn't recognize her. She did a complete one hundred eighty-degree turnaround for this guy. At least David and I haven't changed. We respect and admire each other — the way we are. That's what's important."

"You're absolutely right, Kim," said her mother. "You do have to compromise sometimes, though. I mean, you can't always just plow ahead on your own path intent on preserving your own precious identity. Sometimes you just have to give up part of yourself to another person. You see, when you really love someone, you don't even see it as 'giving up' anything — it's more like you're gaining something precious."

"Well, I suppose it's kind of like the way I feel about ghosts: If I ever see one, I'll believe in them. If your overpowering version of love ever walks up to me, turning me into someone other than myself, then maybe I'll become a believer. In the meantime, I think I'll just go along being plain old Kimberly Barrie, radical and cook."

"I didn't know radicals cooked," quipped her mother with a grin.

"Ah . . . don't confuse me, lady." Kim laughed and tossed a dish towel on her mother's head.

"Heavens, look at the time!" exclaimed Mrs. Barrie. "Your father will be here any minute and I haven't even thought about dinner."

"Maybe we should order a pizza," suggested Kim.

"Ha, ha," said her mother. "No sooner have we convinced him that we're real cooks with a legitimate catering service, than we present him with a store-bought pizza! Don't you realize that could set our reputations back a couple of centuries?"

"Mom, it's six-thirty! He's already five minutes late. We don't have time to even plan another menu."

"You're right. What did you say the name of that pizza joint was?" asked her mother, going for the telephone.

"Harry's," replied Kim with a giggle.

"Oh, well, that sure sounds authentically Italian," joked her mother, leafing through the phone book. "I just hope the pizza is better than the name of the joint."

Mrs. Barrie was just about to reach for the phone when it rang loudly. Kim and her mother both jumped.

"It's for you dear. David," whispered her mother, holding her hand over the receiver.

Kim walked over to the phone, wishing her heart would pound with joy and expectation. It didn't. But the minute she heard David's voice, the warmth of familiarity flooded through her.

"So," he asked, "are you still coming up this weekend?"

"Gee, David, I'm not sure. Remember I told you about Earthly Delights?"

"Uh . . . mmmmmm."

"You remember, the catering service."

"Oh, yeah . . . right."

"Well . . . things are really starting to hop. I think I should stay here and help Mother."

It was then Kim noticed her mother gesturing wildly with her hands.

"Excuse me, David," said Kim. "Mom seems to be trying to say something; either that or she's taken up some kind of exotic Thai dancing."

"Kimberly Barrie," chided her mother good-naturedly, "you've been planning this trip to see David since we left Pittsburgh. I want you to go. And don't let me hear any more about it. I can cope with the Fitches on my own — no problem. Who knows, it might liberate me completely if I manage to carry this thing off by myself."

"Just for that, I'll go." Kim laughed. "David, I'll be on the eight-thirty train out of Washington

Saturday morning. I don't remember what time it gets in. See you then, okay?"

"Sure . . . I'll be there."

Even the sound of the phone clicking dead seemed extra hollow and empty to Kim. She and David used to have some great conversations. That was one of the things she admired so much about him: It seemed as though he could talk about almost any subject. But just now, she thought, that was about the most disappointing conversation she'd ever had with anyone.

"So, do you think I'm completely wack-o?" asked Phoebe, flopping back on her bed and staring at the ceiling. Phoebe was glad her parents let her friends come over, even though she was still grounded. It was always good to talk to Chris.

"Of course you're wack-o," replied Chris, carefully applying the top coat of polish to her nails. "That's what I like so much about you. You keep reminding me of how dumb it is to be serious all the time."

"Well, I'm going to be the serious one now. Should I just put this whole Griffin thing out of my mind? Forget he ever existed?"

"If you want to forget one of the happiest parts of your entire life, sure, go ahead," said Chris, waving her hands in the air to dry the polish. "I've never seen you happier than when that jerk was around, Phoebe. You seemed to be bubbling over. All the time."

"Yeah . . . " sighed Phoebe. "It felt so good to just let go and feel great. I'd been worrying about Brad and me for so long — getting so sick of trying to be perfect for him — I didn't realize how down I'd gotten. It was like I was a bird in a cage, then along came Griffin and set me free. But what am I supposed to do now? I feel like I'm crashing back to earth at the speed of light."

"Hang on, Pheeb. Take it one step at a time. If Woody gets that agent's number, it can't hurt to call, can it? It seems to me you've just got to get an answer one way or the other, right?"

"Hopefully one way and not the other," said Phoebe. "But you're right. I have to know *something*, even if it's bad news."

Why can't I see things as clearly and logically as Chris? Phoebe wondered. But she also remembered the time when Chris's rigid thinking and strict playing by the rules had made her life miserable and almost driven Ted away.

"So how are Brad and Brenda doing?" asked Phoebe, changing the subject as she tried on one of Chris's lipsticks.

"Do you really want to know, or are you just in a mood to torture yourself?" asked Chris, pulling a comb through her cascade of thick blond hair. As with everything about Chris, each hair seemed to know its exact place and fell back into a perfect curtain around her head. Phoebe wished her own hair would tame so easily. It had a life of its own and took off in a million directions whenever she undid her braid. Last year when they'd had art history together, Chris told her she looked positively pre-Raphaelite. That sounded very exotic and romantic at the time, but when the class ended, so had Phoebe's enthusiasm for looking pre-Raphaelite. She and her hair continued to do battle, and most of the time Phoebe had the feeling she was losing.

"I guess I really don't want to know," sighed Phoebe, picking at the bobbles on the striped bedspread. She had accepted the relationship between her old boyfriend and Chris's stepsister. But she couldn't deny it still hurt sometimes. "How are you and Brenda doing, anyway?" It had been tough in the beginning when Chris's dad married Brenda's mom and the two girls found themselves suddenly thrown together. Chris had dealt with it by being even more perfect — although she had ended up putting too much pressure on herself. Brenda had run away.

"We're getting along better than ever," said Chris enthusiastically. "I mean, after I had the brains to give her half a chance, I'm discovering she's really a good person." Chris hesitated. "And I think she's good for Brad; loosening him up a bit."

"I guess I was always too busy trying to shape up into what he wanted me to be to think of trying to help him relax a bit," said Phoebe quietly. Then she added, "Maybe we could make it now."

"Phoebe," chided Chris. "You know that's dumb."

Chris was right; Phoebe knew that. She just wished something would work out with *someone*. It was so hard not having a boyfriend. She liked the warmth and security of a close relationship. She liked caring for someone special, and missed it very much.

Chapter 3

Woody took a deep breath. Now this was his kind of day — so clear the light seemed to burn its images into the very center of his brain. And fresh and crisp. He felt as if he could cycle all the way to the ocean and back before dinner. His body was charged and ready to go.

"So how many pledges have you got for the run-a-thon?"

"Huh . . . what?" Woody turned toward the sound of the voice and immediately a wide smile broke out on his face. Kim was standing about two feet away, mischievously smiling up at him. For the first time, he noticed what beautiful eyes she had. They were usually so hard to see under the mop of hair that fell over her face; but with the sun full on her face, he saw the yellow lights flickering in their green depths.

"Sneaking up on a guy, huh? Well, you'll be pleased to know you just about gave me a heart attack. Nothing I can't recover from, with a little extra consideration, and kindness, and tender loving care, and. . . . "

"All right, all right," said Kim, laughing. "I get the message. But first, how many pledges do you have?"

"You're ruthless, absolutely ruthless. The fact is, I don't jog."

"You have two legs, don't you?" Kim's grin widened.

"Now, let's see," said Woody, bending over at the waist and staring at his knees. "One . . . two. Yep, two legs. How'd you know?"

Kim burst into laughter. "Don't you ever talk straight?" she asked.

Woody immediately snapped to attention, saluting smartly. "This straight enough for you, ma'am?"

Kim groaned.

"Actually I'm a cyclist," continued Woody. "I don't think man would have invented the wheel if we'd been intended to jog from place to place."

"How do you know *woman* didn't invent the wheel?" challenged Kim.

"Come to think of it, she probably did," said Woody with mock seriousness. "Some burly cavewoman probably bashed some poor, old caveman over the head with her rolling pin — it broke in two — and when she saw the loose half roll away — presto, she got the idea for the wheel. So, I stand corrected. *Woman* invented the wheel so I didn't have to jog. Can I ride my bike in this thing?"

"Oh, come on Woody. You can help out with a

good cause," pleaded Kim, ignoring Woody's attempt to tease her. "We really need all the support we can get."

"Okay. Okay. For you, I'll do it. But it's like entering a fish in a fly-a-thon, I tell you. Jogging doesn't come naturally to me. Not at all."

"Ever hear of flying fish?" quipped Kim, then added, "Besides, I bet you'll be the best out there."

Woody's face flushed bright red.

"Why not come downtown with me now, and help scare up some pledges?" she said.

"Sure," he readily agreed, and hopped on his bike. This was definitely one girl you didn't argue with. He cycled along, wondering if she was always so determined. Did she ever really need anyone?

Kim watched him weave deftly through the heavy, after-school traffic. He obviously knew what he was doing, she thought as she pedaled furiously to keep up with him.

"You're amazing," Woody said when they stopped for a light. "How'd you manage to keep up with me?"

"Are you suggesting that I should be slower because I'm a girl?" queried Kim.

"Easy . . . easy. That's your interpretation, not mine," shot back Woody. "I mean no one — and that means male or female — has ever been able to keep up with me in traffic. Dodging cars is my specialty."

Kim felt sort of deflated. Maybe Woody wasn't a typical male chauvinist, she thought. But she was nevertheless glad the light switched before she had to go into some lengthy apology.

"Why don't we leave our bikes here and walk down one side of Main Street, then back up the other?" suggested Woody.

"Good idea," agreed Kim.

At that moment they both leaned down to lock their bikes. For a second they were at eye level, and their eyes met. Kim swallowed hard. What a great face Woody had. Every muscle seemed to be almost under its own control; his features were constantly changing.

"Uh . . . here, I'll get them," said Woody hoarsely. "Might as well just use one lock. Put them together."

"Yeah . . . good thinking," said Kim somewhat breathlessly, relieved to have the excuse to stand up and get out of the way. She had that out-of-control, disoriented feeling again. For a second Main Street didn't even look familiar to her, and she couldn't focus on whether she was in Dallas, or Pittsburgh, or Rose Hill.

"Let's go knock 'em dead," said Woody, flourishing a sheet of pledge forms. In a flash it all came back to Kim. Her breath escaped in a rush.

"Right, partner," she said. "What do you say we aim for ten pledges today?"

"That's a pretty tall order, isn't it?"

"Yeah, but I know most of the people who own stores here. That should help," added Kim.

They ambled slowly down the street. The late afternoon sun bathed everything in a rich, yellow glow, making the expensive boutiques and specialty shops look even ritzier. Even the farmers market had a handsome Georgian facade.

"How come you know everyone down here?" asked Woody.

"My mom and I run a catering business — Earthly Delights. We have to buy a lot of our specialty stuff down here. Plus, Mr. Moser on the corner of Elm is the best butcher in the area. We never go anywhere else."

"You cook?" he asked in surprise.

"As a matter of fact, I love to cook," she said. "I hope to study in Paris one day and be a professional chef."

"You do?" he said dumbfounded. "How'd you get into cooking anyway?"

"I don't know. I just always liked to fool around with different ingredients when I was a kid and one day — what do you know? — I was cooking. It's so cool to see how you can completely change a recipe by adding a little of this or a little of that, how even the weather affects certain dishes. Cooking is really a science, you know."

"To you, maybe," broke in Woody. "To me, cooking is hard labor. Eating is my specialty."

Kim laughed. "Someday I'll have to try out some of my new recipes on you."

"I'd be honored to be your guinea pig," said Woody, bowing dramatically.

"Better wait till you've tasted them," joked Kim.

"Well, here's our first stop," announced Woody. "Break a leg."

Kim bounded up the stairs to the butcher shop. "Good afternoon, Mr. Moser. Has the New Zealand lamb come in yet?"

"Hello there, Kim," responded the butcher. He was short and fat, with a red face. To Kim he always looked a little like the hams he had hanging in the window. "Not yet, but you can be sure Earthly Delights will be the first place I'll call when it does. Should have been here last week. I'll keep you posted. What else can I do for you? I've got some prime roast beef on sale this week. It's a good deal."

"Well, actually, Mr. Moser, I'm not shopping today. I need your help," she began. "The girls' track team at Kennedy needs to make some extra money to meet our budget for the year. We're having a run-a-thon and are asking people to pledge so much per quarter mile. Can you help out?"

Mr. Moser scowled. "I thought the school board took care of things like that."

"It should," agreed Kim, somewhat taken aback. "As a matter of fact the boys get pretty much what they need, but the girls have come up a bit short. We need an extra five hundred to a thousand dollars for equipment and stuff."

"I can't see why you girls want to compete with the boys anyway. Who ever heard of girls being all sweaty with big muscles?" Mr. Moser turned away and began sponging off his counter.

Kim tensed, gripping Woody's arm to keep from saying what was on her mind.

"Mr. Moser, did you say that lamb was coming all the way from New Zealand?" Woody asked, breaking the silence. Mr. Moser turned to him with a confused look.

"Yes . . . it's the usual spring shipment."

"Well, I was just reading in the paper this morning that the Department of Immigration and Naturalization is so backed up, it'll be months before they get things sorted out. That could be what's holding up your lamb."

Mr. Moser looked even more confused. He turned to Kim and rolled his eyes toward the ceiling. "Your friend feeling okay? You haven't let him stand out in the sun too long or anything, have you?"

Kim shook her head. She didn't have a clue what Woody was up to.

"What does the Department of Immigration and Naturalization have to do with the delay in my lamb shipment?" asked Mr. Moser.

"Everything," Woody answered excitedly. "Don't you see? Those poor little lambs are still waiting for their visas, and you know no one gets in this country without a visa these days. If I were you, I'd advertise summer lamb, not spring lamb. According to the article I read it could be quite awhile."

Kim started to giggle. The stern look on Mr. Moser's face began to fade, and the corners of his mouth turned up. Soon all three were laughing.

"Pulling my leg, eh? You kids are too much for me," said Mr. Moser. "Okay Kim, what do you need? After all, you help me out — why shouldn't I help you out, right?"

Kim didn't waste a second. "We were thinking along the lines of a quarter for every quarter of a mile. What do you think?"

"Well, if it's you who'll be doing the running,

I'd rather contribute a dollar for every quarter mile and hope you poop out before you go too far. I wouldn't want to go overboard for girls' athletics, after all."

"Thanks a lot, Mr. Moser. That's very generous of you. Would you please sign this form?" Kim slipped on her glasses and read aloud the conditions of the run-a-thon.

While Mr. Moser scribbled his name on the dotted line, the door to his shop opened and two expensively dressed women walked in.

"Okay, ladies," called out Mr. Moser jovially. "Can't do a thing for you today until you make a pledge to the Kennedy High track team. These kids are working real hard."

The ladies were obviously taken aback, but began filling out the forms without protest.

The butcher winked at Kim and Woody. "You've been getting pledges for two to three dollars a quarter mile, haven't you, kids?" he said when the ladies hesitated before filling in the amount on the pledge line.

"Oh, indeed," came in Woody. "At least. People have been most generous." Woody and Mr. Moser grinned at each other. Kim was holding her breath to keep from cracking up. Woody was such a comedian. She couldn't believe how deftly he'd brought Mr. Moser around.

The women completed their forms, made their purchases, and left hastily. Kim couldn't hold it in any longer, and she burst into laughter. The other two joined in.

"Thanks a lot, Mr. Moser," she said. "You're great. We really appreciate it."

She and Woody turned to leave.

"Son," Mr. Moser called after them, "don't believe everything you read. Those lambs have had their visas for months. I signed them myself. I'm a special agent."

"Right, Mr. Moser," said Woody, saluting, as they slipped out the door. By the time they hit the sidewalk Kim was laughing so hard she didn't watch where she was going and tripped over Woody's heels. She grabbed him to keep from falling and his arms automatically went out to steady her. For a moment they held each other. Kim was the first to pull away. Her heart was pounding.

"Uh, well . . . that was certainly a successful stop," she said. "Thanks to you. Whew. I thought Mr. Moser was going to take me apart at first. We've always been such good friends, too. I don't get it."

"Let's put it this way," said Woody. "To Mr. Moser, women in kitchens make sense; women on track teams overload his circuits."

Kim giggled. "I keep imagining all these lost little lambs standing in endless lines in Auckland waiting for visas to be hung around their necks."

"Well, I had to say something, didn't I?" said Woody. "It was the first thing that came to mind. Really pretty dumb, now that I think about it."

"But it worked," added Kim. "And how."

"You know," said Woody suddenly, "you look sexy in glasses."

Kim's face went bright red. "Oh, Woody. You really are crazy," she said, quickly removing the red-rimmed glasses.

"No, I'm serious," he continued. "They suit you."

"Well, if you want to know the honest truth, I hate them."

"I think you look kind of funky."

"Thank you, Mr. Webster. I'll have that put on my tombstone one day: HERE LIES KIMBERLY BARRIE, COMPLETE WITH GLASSES. SHE WAS KIND OF FUNKY."

They giggled and pushed through the doors of the farmers' market at the same time.

Shouldn't have any trouble here, thought Kim, still tingling all over from Woody's compliment. She knew the old couple who ran the store, Mr. and Mrs. Stenson, very well. They always let her pick through the bins of vegetables to find the perfect ones. Kim confidently approached the gray-haired woman in the flowered bib apron. "Hello, Mrs. Stenson," Kim said.

"Well hi, Kim," Mrs. Stenson responded cheerfully. "What brings you in today?"

"For once I'm not shopping for my mom. I came to see if you would like to make a pledge to support the girls' track team at my high school?"

"Well, Kim, I just don't know," said Mrs. Stenson, shaking her head. "Let me go get Alf."

Mr. Stenson walked to his wife's side. They conferred in whispers. Kim gave Woody a worried look. Getting pledges was no easy job, she was beginning to realize.

"Kim, honey, you know we'd love to contribute, but we're selling the shop this spring," began Mr. Stenson. "Retiring, you know. We've had this place here about forty years. Started it back when Rose Hill was just a little bump on the road to Washington. We've seen a lot of changes, haven't we, Mother?"

Mrs. Stenson smiled wistfully. "We sure have, Alf." She put her arm around his waist. They were a perfect fit.

Kim couldn't help smiling. What a sweet couple. She and David never even held hands in public. David said it looked as if they were in junior high.

"Yeah . . . I've got a real soft spot for this town," continued Mr. Stenson with a faraway smile.

"Well, how about a soft spot for the Kennedy High girls' track team?" suggested Woody, absentmindedly picking up a few tangerines. "We're trying to get the whole town behind them."

Mr. Stenson came slowly back to the present. "I don't know, son. Of course I'd love to help, but it seems like we've always got someone coming through that door asking for a contribution to this or that."

Slowly Woody started tossing the tangerines into the air. Kim watched wide-eyed. What in the world was he up to now? Finally, there were six tangerines flying around in a circle as Woody juggled away. Mr. and Mrs. Stenson stared in disbelief.

"Where'd you learn to do that?" asked Mr. Stenson in awe. "I've been trying to do that for years. Right, Mother?"

"Here," said Woody, nimbly catching all the

tangerines one after another. "Start with just two." While Mrs. Stenson and Kim looked on, Woody showed Mr. Stenson how to juggle. In ten minutes he had the motion down. His face beamed.

"Look here, Mother!" he called. "I'm juggling!"

"You are one fast learner, Mr. Stenson," said Woody, clapping the grocer on the back. "Well, Kim, I guess we'd better get going. We're not doing very well with our pledges." He turned to Mr. Stenson. "But I certainly have enjoyed meeting you. I hope you get a good price for your store. And, Mr. Stenson, you keep practicing. I'll come back in a couple of weeks to see how you're doing."

"Uh . . . listen, son," said Mr. Stenson, rubbing his chin. "What'd you say you were collecting money for?"

"The girls' track team up at Kennedy High," Woody replied enthusiastically. "They've got one of the best teams in the state, but unless we can come up with about a thousand dollars, they're going to be walking to their meets and wearing hand-me-down shorts."

"I think we can pitch in our share. What do you say, Mother?"

"This town's been very good to us, Alf. It wouldn't hurt us to give back some," said Mrs. Stenson.

"What's the going rate?" asked Mr. Stenson. Kim readily explained.

"Then what do you say we give fifty cents a

40

quarter mile?" Mr. Stenson said. "Does that sound about right?"

"That's wonderful, Mr. Stenson!" burst out Kim. "Thanks a lot. Here's a copy of our track meet schedule in case you could make it to any of the meets. We'd love to have you there."

Woody and Kim backed out of the store, still exchanging waves and smiles with the old couple.

"Woody, you are a truly amazing person," said Kim quietly. "You were so nice to the Stensons."

"It's not hard being nice to people like that," said Woody. "They make me believe in 'happily ever after.' "

"I know what you mean."

Kim and Woody walked along in silence for a while. Kim was still in awe of Woody's performance. She could tell that being kind to the Stensons had come naturally to him. Kim was beginning to realize how sensitive he was — not to mention smart and funny.

What am I doing, thought Kim suddenly, talking myself into falling for this guy? She glanced over at Woody. He seemed lost in thought, too. His mop of curly hair bounced softly around his head with each stride of his long legs, and his usually animated features had taken on a gentle, faraway look.

"Penny for your thoughts," said Kim.

"Hey, if you've got the money, I've got the thoughts." The clown had re-emerged, and Kim knew he wasn't going to confess what he'd been thinking.

"Where to now?" she asked.

"You tell me. This is your show," said Woody with a playful grin.

"Oh, yeah? You're doing a great job of running it." For an instant Woody looked defensive. Kim laughed. "Calm down. For once I'm not on the attack. I mean it. You're so fantastic with people — I don't know what I'd have done without you." All at once she felt she'd said too much. Blood rushed to her face, and her cheeks burned. "Uh . . . how about Betty's Beauty Salon. Is it worth a try?" she asked quickly.

"Lead on, Macduff," said Woody dramatically. "A bunch of women under hair dryers are definitely in a vulnerable position. We should make a killing there."

"Ah . . . ha, so you do have a malicious streak!" cried Kim playfully. "I knew it would come out sooner or later."

"Look," he retorted, "anything to make a buck, right?"

Once inside, Kim made her spiel about the girls' track team, then stood back to give Woody center stage. He wandered from chair to chair throwing a compliment out here, making a funny suggestion there, pretending to put curlers in his hair, mimicking the manicurist. In five minutes, the place was in an uproar. They left with six more pledges.

"Are we some kind of great team or what?" said Woody, bouncing down the street.

"Yeah, I'm the manager and you're the whole show."

"That's nuts," said Woody, playfully rumpling her hair. "I'm some clown. I'll admit that. But

I'd never be able to keep it together and remember I was supposed to get signatures, pledges, and stuff. I'd get home at the end of the day thinking I'd done such a super job only to find a pocketful of empty slips. No, I think we're a perfect team."

Kim didn't know what he meant — and she wasn't sure what she wanted him to mean. They were having so much fun, best just leave it at that.

"Okay, okay, enough for today," said Woody finally. "I've officially had enough."

"Whew . . . me, too," agreed Kim. She felt exhausted.

"Listen, I've got a great idea," said Woody, spinning around on his heels. "Meet you back at the bikes in two minutes." Then he took off down the street. Kim stared after him in wonder. What was he up to now? She shook her head and walked slowly down the street. No, she'd never, ever met anyone like Woody Webster.

Kim was unlocking the bikes when Woody returned with a brown bag.

"What have you got?" she asked, handing him his bike.

"Surprise. Follow me."

For once Kim didn't ask a lot of questions. Somehow she knew this was going to be interesting. Woody really knew how to make things come alive. No wonder everyone liked him so much.

She had a hard time keeping up with him this time, as he tore through the downtown streets. Finally, the last traffic light was behind them and they were winding up Rose Hill, the short, steep hill that had given its name to this little town that had only recently blossomed into a real suburb.

"There," said Woody triumphantly, rolling to a halt at the top. They leaned their bikes against the back of the sole bench and sat down. "Isn't that great?"

Kim sucked in her breath. Below them the green hills dropped away in a graceful arc to the Potomac River. The final rays of the sun pierced the tree tops, making them light up like giant candles at the top. The surface of the river was splashed with molten gold. Kim had often been up Rose Hill, but never at this time of the day. This was beautiful.

"Here," said Woody, opening the brown bag and putting two milkshakes on the seat between them. "Mocha Miracle or Strawberry Surprise? The choice is yours."

Kim laughed. "This is the best. Woody Webster, you are something else."

"Save the small talk," replied Woody gruffly, his face reddening. "We've got some serious drinking to do. Mocha or Strawberry?"

"Strawberry, please."

They sat on the bench slurping the shakes, and watching the subtle changes the setting sun made on the world below.

"Boy, I wish I could learn to light a stage like that," said Woody finally. "It seems so easy when the sun does it, but I can tell you, to achieve that special quality of light is super difficult."

"I bet you could do it, though," said Kim. "I

saw that fashion show you put on. It was really something."

"Yeah, it was okay," said Woody, concentrating on his shake.

"Do you think you'll go into the theater professionally?" asked Kim, chasing the last bits of her milkshake around the bottom of the cup with her straw.

"I'd like to," he said. "But it's so competitive. I'd have to have a lot more confidence in my ability before I committed myself."

"Don't you have it?" asked Kim in wonder. Woody seemed to have life by the tail . . . completely under control.

"Not really. I have a lot to learn yet."

"Well, I bet if you put your mind to it you can do it."

"If you have that much faith in me, I guess I'll just have to do it, huh?" He smiled warmly at her. Kim looked quickly away. She wished she hadn't said that. She meant it — she couldn't imagine Woody failing at anything. But now the air between them was charged with an intimacy she didn't know how to handle. She felt lightheaded and disoriented — out of control, again.

Chapter

4

"Heelloo out there, Cardinals. This is your man of the hour, Peter Lacey, of WKND, bringing you music to digest your lunch by. Hey, after what they served us today, you're going to need all the help you can get."

Phoebe rolled her eyes and laughed with the rest of the crowd gathered in the quad. The next instant, the entire area began vibrating to the sounds of heavy-metal rock. Phoebe groaned.

"I wish Lisa would come back," she said, remembering the calming influence of Peter's girl friend who'd gone to Colorado for ice-skating training. As much as Phoebe hoped Lisa's dream of the Olympics would come true, she knew Peter missed his girl friend desperately. "He used to play such nice, mellow music when Lisa was out here listening. This stuff is going to give me indigestion for sure."

"Yeah, you can really tell how much he misses

46

her," said Woody, juggling four of Sasha's pencils as she scribbled away nearby. Phoebe watched the scene with amusement. As editor of the school newspaper, Sasha had developed a famous collection of well-sharpened pencils that were always sticking out of her books and note pads, and from behind her ears. Woody couldn't resist tormenting her by swiping them for improvs. Phoebe's favorite was the time he did a five-minute interview with two of Sasha's pencils, grilling them on what it was really like in the inside world of journalism.

"How are you doing with your money-making, Sasha?" asked Phoebe. Sasha also had been grounded after the accident with Woody's car, and now she was working off her share of the repair bill in her parents' bookstore. Phoebe was surprised to see Sasha's face light up.

"Not too bad," she said, popping a handful of nuts and raisins into her mouth. "I'm really getting to know my way around the store, even if it is from the end of a dust mop."

Phoebe looked at her friend with curiosity. Sasha often took great pleasure in things other people found totally ordinary. That's one reason why Phoebe liked her so much. Phoebe watched a faint blush creep over Sasha's pale cheeks.

"Is there anything you'd like to tell us?" Phoebe asked mischievously.

Sasha smiled shyly. "Well, I don't want to jinx anything, but Wes and I have been getting along really well lately."

"You have?!" exclaimed Phoebe. "That's great!" Phoebe was pleased for her friend, but she couldn't help being a little anxious, too. Wes and Sasha had fallen heavily for each other before, when they'd first met. But they'd been so busy being in love, they hadn't taken time out to really know each other. At first, all Sasha did was sigh constantly, or tell everyone how wonderful Wes was.

When she finally did come up for air, Sasha discovered she and Wes were completely different people — apparently all wrong for any kind of long-term relationship together. It was hard for Sasha to handle the fact that Wes went to Leesburg Military Academy because her parents were anti-war types from the sixties. The last time Phoebe and Sasha had talked about it, Sasha said she and Wes had decided to cool it and just be friends.

"The last three afternoons he came by the store," admitted Sasha, offering Phoebe her bag of trail mix. Phoebe shook her head.

"We're still not sure where it's at," continued Sasha, "but we know we've got something — something pretty special. All we have to do is figure out how to make it all fit into the different kinds of lives we lead."

"Sasha, that's great," said Phoebe. "Good luck! No wonder dusting shelves doesn't bum you out!"

Sasha smiled and turned to Kim. "Don't forget to come by my parents' shop for run-a-thon pledges," she said. "They always like to contribute to stuff like that."

"We should go by there this afternoon," replied Kim, smiling over at Woody. "What do you say?"

"Sure. You call the tune, I'll dance the dance." Woody immediately slipped into a Gene Kelly routine, running up the back of the bench, leaping off, and clicking his heels in midair. Kim joined in the laughter.

"Hey look, a body's got to keep warm, you know," he said, winding up with a little tap dance. "And speaking of bodies keeping warm, those two are about to catch on fire." He pointed at Chris and Ted walking slowly toward the group, their arms wrapped around each other. It didn't seem quite right to Kim, to walk around openly displaying your feelings like that. But then she thought of Mr. and Mrs. Stenson as they stood in their shop, their arms linked as if it were the most natural thing in the world. A lump rose in her throat. It was a simple gesture, but it let people know what was important to them in life: each other.

"Hope you enjoyed that little lunchtime lullaby," said Peter when the music finally wore itself out into blessed silence. "I'm sure you all recognized the pure, sweet tones of Led Zeppelin." The crackling sound of paper being unfolded came over the speaker. "Mr. Cilento wants me to remind all you smokers that if you must smoke, please don't exhale. Uh . . . just kidding. He did say you were straying farther and farther from the smoking areas, and would like it stopped. So, back to the corral, gang. Okay?"

"Smoking shouldn't even be allowed," said Sasha firmly. Kim watched the wind pick up Sasha's wavy hair strand by strand and float it gently on the breeze. She looked pale and dramatic, and very vulnerable. "The school is promoting bad health habits by even having a smoking area. I'm going to suggest at the next student council meeting that it be abolished."

"But Sasha — " Kim started.

"How are you doing with the prom design?" broke in Woody, turning to Janie Barstow and Henry Braverman, who were sitting quietly on the sidelines holding hands. With Woody's encouragement and the prom committee's approval, they were making huge posters of clothing designs to decorate the walls of the gym for the prom. The theme was "Springtime in Paris."

"Pretty good," said Henry, smiling self-consciously.

"They're wonderful," said Janie, her silky, brown hair tumbling softly around her sensitive features. "Absolutely wonderful. I think you'll be impressed."

"My mom has a couple of nineteen-forties' dresses from Paris," broke in Sasha, "if you want to borrow them for ideas. She got them in an antique shop there last fall, so they're the real thing."

"Sure," Henry said excitedly. "That would be great. We've mostly been working from pictures of paintings."

"Well, I have an Yves St. Laurent tie you could use," joked Ted.

"Ted Mason, you lie!" Chris laughed. "I've never even seen you in a tie."

"You mean I've never invited you up to view my extensive collection of exotic ties, my dear?"

Ted said in a mock leer, rubbing his hands to-gether as he winked slyly at Henry. Chris swatted playfully at his head.

Janie laughed, her cheeks glowing bright pink. Henry put his arm around her shoulders and held her close.

"I think this is going to be the best prom ever, thanks to you two," declared Sasha. "It's going to be so much fun to write up for the paper. I can't wait."

Kim watched Janie and Henry acknowledge the compliment with shy smiles; she could tell they were really pleased.

When she had first come to Rose Hill, Kim couldn't figure out these two. They were the only ones of this boisterous crew who weren't out-going. They seemed to like being included but still stayed on the fringes of all the crazy activity.

Kim was glad that they'd come this far. She'd heard about the hard time they'd had in high school before meeting each other. She'd even seen pictures of Janie in an old yearbook and could hardly believe this was the same girl. Back then her hair had been nondescript and almost covered her eyes, as if she was hiding from something. From all Kim heard, it seemed that Janie had gone out of her way to make herself unattractive. It sounded like a classic case of insecurity.

She was puzzled until Woody told her about the terrible mixup at homecoming when Peter had asked Janie to help him be deejay that eve-ning. At that time Janie had had such a crush on him, she'd interpreted this as a date, and when she discovered that Lisa was his date for the evening, she'd been shattered.

And Kim could hardly believe what Henry had been through. His dad was super jock, head coach of the local college, and he naturally expected his nice, tall son to follow in his Adidas-sprung footsteps. But Henry had no interest in sports and lied to his father about joining the basketball team so his dad would get off his case, and Henry would go back to his drawing board.

Wow, thought Kim. She'd thought she'd had a rough time just because she had to change schools so many times. But then Janie and Henry had found each other. Kim loved the story of how the couple had met, by chance, in an empty classroom and hadn't been apart since. Their relationship had changed both their lives — giving Henry the strength to confront his father with his ambition to be a designer, and Janie had suddenly blossomed. Her long-hidden beauty was enhanced by her sensitive, generous nature.

A shiver ran down Kim's back as she watched them talking to Woody. Their story was so romantic, and had happened to people she actually knew. Again she wondered if she judged love too harshly. Maybe her mother was right — maybe by getting lost in someone else, just a little, you could discover more about yourself.

"And this is Peter Lacey, signing off for the day. I hope you've enjoyed this hour of top entertainment . . . and the music." Everyone groaned again. Peter could make what Kim considered the world's worst jokes, but for some reason everyone always laughed. Maybe his remarks were so funny because they were so dumb. Like elephant jokes. Or maybe it was just that all the kids liked Peter so much.

"Can it, Lacey," shouted Woody at the outdoor speaker. "Hire yourself a decent script writer."

"But first I want to remind all you bozos," continued Peter, "to get out and round up those pledges for the run-a-thon. You've got two weeks left and I think we all agree this is one worthy cause. Tell 'em Peter Lacey of WKND sent you."

Kim smiled. She'd have to thank Peter for all his support. Every day since she'd announced the run-a-thon, he'd ended his broadcast with a reminder to help.

"Oh, Kim," said Chris, moving gracefully through the crowd. "Ted and I want to sign up. I think we can manage a few laps." She turned to Ted with a grin. "At least I know I can. I can't vouch for our macho quarterback here. He tends to go to seed after the football season."

Ted grinned back and immediately hoisted Chris into the air. Chris squealed.

"You can't come down till you take that back," said Ted, bouncing her up and down.

"Ted Mason, you put me down this minute!" Chris giggled, her long blond hair falling around his face and down the front of his navy cable-knit sweater.

"Say 'uncle,'" demanded Ted.

"I won't. You can't make me."

"You're right, but I don't have to let you down,

either. We'll see how far to seed I've gone." He tossed her into the air, catching her expertly on the way down.

"Okay. Okay. You win. Uncle. Aunt. Siamese twins. Anything!" Chris laughed. Ted set Chris gently on the ground. Both were red-faced and breathing hard. "Okay, Kim, I guess he made his point. Sign us both up. Ted can carry me on his back all the way around the track."

Ted threatened to pick her up again. Chris stepped neatly out of the way, grabbing the scarf from around his neck as she did.

"Women!" he said with mock exasperation. "What do you say, Woody? Are they worth it?"

Woody glanced quickly over at Kim. His face colored instantly, as he stammered out some answer.

"Brenda," called Chris, waving wildly toward the auditorium door. "Over here."

Brenda broke into a run to get there. Brenda was beautiful in a dark, secretive sort of way. Her hair was brushed back from her face and her large, dark eyes were luminous. She approached them enthusiastically. Whatever had been wrong in Brenda's life at one time was definitely right now, thought Kim.

"Hi, everyone," said Brenda gaily, looking funky in her loose, black sweater and straight, hot pink skirt. Her style was such a sharp contrast to Chris's tweedy, conservative look. "How's it going?"

"Now that Peter Lacey's signed off for the day," said Woody, "much better. How are things down at Garfield House?" he asked.

54

"Great. There's been a lot of response since Tony got the word out to the area high schools that a shelter for runaways exists. Everyone's really psyched." As Brenda spoke, she clearly was distracted by something across the quad.

Kim looked over to see Brad Davidson rushing toward the group.

"Guess what?!" he shouted when he was still a long way away. "You won't believe it!"

"You finally flattened John Marquette?" joked Woody about Kennedy's wrestling champion and Brad's archenemy ever since the day he insulted Brenda.

"Ha. Much as I'd like to admit I had," said Brad, "I haven't. I have better news. I just got a letter from Princeton."

"And. . . ?" Everyone breathed at once. Brad had been dreaming of getting into Princeton ever since freshman year. This was one of the first things Kim ever knew about him.

"Naaaaa," he said, turning around and pretending to walk away. "I don't think you're really interested."

"Davidson, cut it out," said Ted, pulling Chris to his side. "Give us the scoop."

"I got in!" he shouted, jumping up and punching the air with his fist. "They want me! Princeton wants me!"

"Way to go, Brad," shouted Woody, leaping off the bench and thumping Brad on the back. "Way to go."

"All right, Davidson," added Ted. "Give me five."

"Oh Brad, that's terrific," said Chris.

"They've got a great newspaper," said Sasha. "They're always winning the grand prize in college journalism."

Kim joined the group clustered around him. They all talked at once. Finally Brad pushed through and grabbed Brenda. "So what do you think, babe? Looks like I might finally make something of myself."

Brenda laughed, her wide-set eyes brimming over with love and admiration. Kim laughed, too. Brad was already student body president, and involved with just about every other committee and organization at the school. She was sure no one ever doubted he'd get into Princeton, but she knew how much it meant to him. "I love you," she heard Brenda whisper in his ear. "I'm so proud of you."

"I love you, too," he whispered back and they giggled like conspirators. Kim felt embarrassed about overhearing this private exchange.

The bell rang. Slowly the crowd broke up, people wandering off in different directions. Kim knew Woody had class in the room right next door next period. She started over to him, so they could walk together. But at that moment, he threw his arms around Phoebe's shoulders and they headed off, heads bent close together in conversation. Kim stopped dead, watching them disappear. Suddenly she felt lonely.

"You got it?!" cried Phoebe. "Griffin's agent? You got the name?"

"I think it's the one. Called Act I. Run by some guy called David Solomon. It's a big deal operation according to my mom. She was pretty impressed that they'd been interested in him. I guess he's as good as we thought he was."

"Oh, of course he is. He's wonderful," bubbled Phoebe.

"Mom didn't have a number for them, but you can get it from information," continued Woody, patting her hand. "I hope it works out for you, kid. You've been looking down for too long. It's springtime. Time to snap out of the old winter funk. Time to come back to the sub shop and make yourself sick eating too much pepperoni."

Phoebe smiled warmly up into his face. She put her arms around him and kissed him lightly on the cheek. "Thanks, Woody. You're a real friend."

Kim drew in a deep breath. Her chest burned with pain, and her eyes stung with tears. She watched Woody and Phoebe a moment longer. What was wrong with her? Was she jealous of other people's closeness? Was she jealous of Phoebe? Kim squeezed her eyes shut to stop the tears and walked off in the opposite direction.

"Act I?" said Phoebe into the receiver. She still couldn't believe she was calling New York, or that she might soon be talking to Griffin. The hope of making contact with him had kept her going for such a long time. Now she was almost there. "Is this Act I?"

"It is," came back a woman's efficient reply. She sounded so professional, she threw Phoebe into confusion. Phoebe swallowed hard, trying to hear herself think above the pounding of her heart.

"Uh . . . I'm trying to get in touch with a friend of mine . . . an actor," she said nervously. "Griffin Neill. He's with your agency."

"That doesn't sound familiar. Are you certain we represent him?"

"I think so," said Phoebe. "May I speak to Mr. Solomon, please?"

"Mr. Solomon isn't in. Leave your phone number and he'll get back to you later."

Phoebe had barely gotten the number out when the woman hung up. Phoebe stared at the dead phone in her hand, listening to it buzz maddeningly at her. She stared for so long a recording came on asking her to "hang up and dial again."

That's exactly what I'll do, thought Phoebe, and she redialed the number. That woman had scared her so much she hadn't been able to think. Now she was going to get her information. She had to. This number was her only connection to Griffin. The same woman answered.

"I thought I told you that Mr. Solomon would call you later," she said when Phoebe explained who she was.

"I know you did," said Phoebe apologetically. "But, you see, it's very important that I get in touch with Griffin Neill. It's an emergency." Phoebe didn't like to lie; but as far as she was concerned, it was an emergency. She was going to go crazy if she didn't get in touch with Griffin. Going crazy definitely sounded like an emergency to her.

"I'm terribly sorry," said the woman. "The fact is I simply can't give out information about our clients — if he is a client. Not to you. Not to anyone. It's policy. You can understand that, can't you?"

Phoebe had to agree the woman had a point, however frustrating it might be.

"Well . . . please, could you give Griffin a message?"

"Sure. I can do that."

"Tell him to call Phoebe. Tell him it's urgent. Tell him . . . I need him . . . to call."

"Okay. I'll put it up on the board. He's sure to see it if he comes in."

Again the phone went dead, and again Phoebe was left with that empty feeling that all her efforts had been in vain. "If he comes in!" Phoebe wanted to scream with frustration.

Chapter 5

Kim felt a tug of homesickness as the train wound slowly toward Pittsburgh. Pittsburgh had been home for three years. Longer than anywhere else, unless she counted the four years they'd been in Dallas, but she'd been too young to remember that. It had been in Pittsburgh that she experienced her first days of high school, worn her first pair of panty hose, and shaved her legs for the first time. She smiled at the memory. She'd borrowed her father's razor and locked herself in the bathroom one Saturday afternoon. Then she'd worn jeans for a whole week thinking the entire world would be mad at her. Her father had complained about the razor, bemoaning the fact that the quality of steel had gone down. And her mother had bought Kim her own razor when she'd found out. It had taken her weeks to talk herself into shaving her legs again.

She'd attended her first NOW meeting at the

Pittsburgh Y and bought her first makeup at Woolworth's on Delavier Street. Pittsburgh's huge old maple trees had provided deep shadows for her first kiss with David, her first real boyfriend. They'd been walking through Rushmore Park coming back from the movies when it happened. But how had it happened? Had he held her hand, then tenderly brought her to his chest and found her mouth? Kim couldn't remember. Knowing David, he'd probably asked permission before even trying. Good old practical, organized, and proper David.

Kim sighed, then glanced at her watch. It was hard to imagine that she would be seeing David again in just about five minutes. Two months was a long time. She lived in Rose Hill now. Now the high school team she rooted for was the Cardinals, not the Miners. And her city's football team was the Redskins, not the Steelers. It was strange how easily one could keep changing loyalties. Was anything permanent? Maybe life was just a cloud of bubbles that could burst at any time. Maybe it was this that made her so determined to be independent and capable. No one could ever take that away from her; she could stand on her own two feet. That wouldn't change, no matter how many times she moved.

Kim giggled, her mind switching thoughts faster than the train switched tracks in the final mile to the station. She could still see Woody leaping off the bench like Gene Kelly gone berserk. She thought of his curly mop of hair bouncing around and his bright face glowing with an energy that seemed to come from every fiber of his being. Kim felt a tingling down her spine. What a riot he was. What fun. He made her feel crazily alive, capable of any madness . . . and practically out of control. Kim frowned. She didn't like feeling out of control. This was what bothered her about Woody. This and his obvious attraction to Phoebe. Kim couldn't understand that relationship at all. How could he act like he liked her so much, then go off and be so intimate with Phoebe?

Well, what do you expect, dummy, Kim chided herself. Woody knows you have a boyfriend. And he knows you've gone all the way to Pittsburgh to visit him this weekend. Woody wasn't the type to put the moves on someone else's girl friend.

The train squeaked to a halt. Kim slung her bag of unread books over her shoulder and stepped onto the platform. She inhaled deeply, held her breath for a second, then exhaled slowly. She desperately wanted to feel excited about the day before her, to feel her knees go weak when she caught sight of David; but instead, as she looked up and down the track, she had to force herself to suppress a yawn. She hadn't slept very well thinking about how much she didn't feel like going to Pittsburgh. But here she was and there was David running down the platform to meet her. She'd forgotten how good-looking he was. His cheeks were flushed, and his black hair glistened in the sun.

"There you are!" he exclaimed, grabbing her bag. "I was beginning to worry. The train was ten minutes late."

"It was?" replied Kim, flipping her watch over

on her wrist. The worn-out band she'd been planning to replace for months came undone and the watch crashed onto the platform. David immediately leaned over to retrieve it.

"You ought to get that fixed," he said, and for some reason this grated on Kim's nerves. She knew it needed fixing. She hadn't come all the way to Pittsburgh to have David Nelson tell her that.

Come on, Kim, she scolded herself. Snap out of it. Give the day a chance, at least. Then all of a sudden she remembered what Woody had done the last time her watch band had broken.

"Hold out your hands," she told David. He looked confused, but complied. Kim put the watch in his upturned palms. "Tell me what that is." She grinned mischievously.

He stared at her watch for a moment, then at her. Shaking his head, he said, "It looks like your broken watch to me."

"No, silly, that's not it: You've got time on your hands." Kim burst out laughing. "Don't you get it — time on your hands?"

"Oh . . . right," said David, with a slight smile. "That's cute. Yeah."

Kim felt another bubble burst. Well, David never did have much of a sense of humor. What did she expect?

"Where would you like to eat?" he asked.

Again Kim felt a wave of disappointment wash over her. She wished he had some neat place all picked out, or a pizza to share in the park. The images of Woody, the impulsive milkshakes, and Rose Hill flashed through her mind.

"I'm in the mood for something ethnic," she said, smiling at David. "Aren't we near the Greek section? How about a little moussaka and baklava? Yum."

"Hmmmmm . . . well . . . ," stammered David. "It makes sense to find something closer by since it's noon now and things will get pretty crowded by one."

One more bubble burst. Good old practical David. "Yeah, I guess you're right," Kim conceded. "There's a burger joint across the street."

They walked over to the fast food restaurant.

"Well, I got into Carnegie-Mellon," announced David, setting his tray down next to hers.

"David, that's terrific!" said Kim. David's big dream was to be president of his own company one day. He loved everything to do with the business world. Kim knew that for him studying business at Carnegie-Mellon was definitely the first step up the ladder of success.

"Yeah, I'm really looking forward to it. I'm ready for some serious study. High school's turning into a real pain. It seems like nobody takes anything seriously there."

Another image of Woody — juggling Sasha's pencils — came to mind. Kim suppressed a giggle. "You're right, but we're only teenagers, after all. Aren't these supposed to be the best years of our lives? We've got plenty of time to take stuff seriously."

"It depends on what you want out of life — if you want to be left behind or not," explained David. "The big corporations aren't going to wait around until the goons of this world decide to go straight. They're looking now. At career night last week, there were representatives from IBM, and Xerox, and Exxon. All the biggies. I had some great talks with these guys, and one thing was clear: They're definitely on the lookout for hard-working, dedicated people. No goof-offs need apply."

Kim wondered what David would think of Woody. Woody was completely outrageous, but he was serious, too, and concerned about other people — and his future. Hardly what she'd call a goof-off. Kim got lost in her memories of the wonderful afternoon they'd spent together getting run-a-thon pledges, as David rambled on and on about the jerks at school.

"So what do you think?" he finally asked.

"Uh. . . ." stammered Kim.

"You're not listening to me, are you?"

Kim hung her head. David looked hurt. She owed him more than that — at least she should try to pay attention to what he was saying. After all, they'd had some good times together.

"I'm sorry, David, I was thinking about Mother catering that tea at the senator's house without me," said Kim quickly. "I hope she can handle it."

"I'm sure she can. Your mother's a very capable woman. How's the business going, anyway?"

"Fine. Really well. I mean, it seems to be picking up steam."

"Maybe you should incorporate. You know, become a private corporation."

"Oh, I don't think we need to do anything like that. We're just a small operation, after all."

"That's okay. If you're pulling in over ten

thousand dollars a year, it's beneficial to incorporate. You get a corporate tax rate that is much lower than the rate you're paying now."

"Really?" said Kim in surprise. "I'll talk to our accountant."

"I'd get a good tax lawyer if I were you," added David. "It'll cost a bit more, but it'll be worth it in the long run."

"Want a job as a consultant?" joked Kim. "I think Earthly Delights could use someone like you."

"I need more experience," said David seriously.

Kim looked at him closely. Being around Woody had definitely put her into a whole different plane of thinking. Now that she was with David, she knew just how different it was. She'd forgotten how serious and practical he was. He hadn't caught on to one of her jokes yet. Well, he'd certainly do great in the business world, that was for sure.

There was an awkward silence. Kim racked her brain for something to say, but it seemed like they'd already said everything they had to say to each other. She concentrated on finishing her lunch, saving the milkshake till last. It reminded her of Woody. Thoughts of her crazy friend were about the only thing keeping her going, it seemed.

"Kim," said David finally in a funny, far-off voice. "What's happening? Things just don't seem to be going real well, do they?"

For a moment Kim wanted to deny that anything was wrong. In so many ways, Rose Hill was still new and uncertain; and Pittsburgh was home. She didn't feel ready to give that up, but she couldn't deny the strain she'd felt between them since stepping down off the train. Her shoulders ached with tension.

"I don't know, David," she said. "Maybe this is what happens when people don't see each other for a while. Maybe we've kind of, you know, lost touch."

"No, it's more than that. It's like we're on two different planets shouting back and forth across the space in between. You only hear part of what I say, and I only hear part of what you say."

Good analogy, thought Kim, admiring David's sharp, analytical mind. Watch out, business world! David Nelson is going to take you by storm. But as these thoughts flashed across her mind, she knew she wasn't made to take that world by storm with him. When they'd first started dating, all they had to agree on was which movie to see. But life wasn't that simple anymore.

"Yeah, maybe we're part of another era that's over now. Maybe we're hanging on to all the wrong things, trying to keep them alive from one hundred fifty miles apart."

"I don't know. I just know something's not working. It makes me feel bad, but I think we're kidding ourselves if we don't recognize it."

Kim looked sadly over at David. If they were both agreeing — if what they were both saying was that it was best to end their relationship here and now — why did it hurt so much?

"We've shared a lot," said David, as if reading

her mind. "We've got some good memories. They'll always be special."

They sat in silence, staring at the half-eaten burgers and cold French fries without seeing them.

"Oh, Kim," said David mournfully. "I always dreaded this day. I wanted to believe that we would go on forever."

"Me, too," said Kim quietly, taking his hand. "I never even dreamed it would happen. Not like this." She smiled. "I thought I was supposed to get mad at you for looking at someone else, then swear I'd never speak to you again."

David laughed softly. "That kind of pain would be easier to deal with. What hurts is, I still like you . . . a lot. But I don't think we can keep going together when we're so far apart. That really hurts."

They lapsed into silence again.

"David?" said Kim, her voice catching in her throat.

"Yes?"

"I think it would be better if I go back to Rose Hill today."

"Oh, Kim," he said, his face drawn with pain. "Do you have to?"

"I think it's best. I'm afraid we'll just hurt each other more if I stay. Don't you agree?"

David hung his head, staring at their entwined fingers. Kim wanted to reach up and run her fingers through his familiar dark hair, but she knew it would be a gesture of desperation. Giving up the past was hard when the future was so uncertain.

"I guess you're right," he said softly.

Again, the painful silence surrounded them.
Finally Kim squeezed his hand. "What do you
say we go for a walk? I don't know about you,
but I need some fresh air."

"Yeah. This room feels about three feet square
and shrinking."

Kim laughed. "Fast."

"Where would you like to go?" asked David
when they'd gotten outside. The sun was warm
and bright, making the buildings in this rundown
section of town seem almost enchanting in an old-
fashioned sort of way.

"Oh, I don't know. Let's just walk and see
where we end up," said Kim, linking her arm
through David's.

For the next two hours they wandered through
the back streets of Pittsburgh, through the Greek
section where Kim picked up a bottle of imported
olive oil for her mother. Then into the Italian
section where they shared a cup of cappucino in
an outdoor cafe. Up one street and down another,
laughing at the funny sights like the little dachs-
hund barking at all the passersby from its fifth-
floor window, and ogling the colorful displays in
the store windows.

Back at the station, they had time for one more
cup of coffee before the train left. Kim knew she
was just trying to forestall the final good-bye. The
afternoon had proved what good friends they'd
always been. They'd had fun. It was hard to
admit that their relationship wasn't going anywhere, that the magic was really over. But it was.

Finally David walked her down to the train.

"Kim — " he started.

"I know, David," she said softly, feeling very hollow inside and very sad. "I know, and I'm sorry, too."

"Yeah, I guess this is it, huh?"

"I think so," she said, wrapping her arms around his waist. Funny, now that they were really breaking up, she felt comfortable showing affection in public. And for the first time, he didn't draw back. "Thank you for a beautiful afternoon."

The train whistle blasted close behind them. They both jumped, then burst out laughing.

"Let's stay in touch," said Kim, kissing him lightly on the cheek before leaping up the stairs. The train was starting to move. It wasn't his faults she remembered as she watched him grow smaller and smaller on the platform as the train drew away, but his good qualities, those things that had first attracted her to him — the funny grin, the sparkling eyes. She raised her hand in a final farewell.

Kim awoke two hours later in Washington. Still half-asleep, she stumbled onto the bus to Rose Hill and settled back for the last leg of her journey. Pittsburgh seemed almost unreal, almost like she'd never been there. But she had, and it was true: She and David had broken up. It was the right decision. She was convinced of that, despite the pain in her heart. Now, through her tears, she felt light and free, eager to get on with her life in Rose Hill. The past — Pittsburgh — was over.

The bus roared down Main Street, past the

butcher's and the farmers market, all the places she'd been to that magical day with Woody. He'd never been out of her mind all day, and now he came rushing back with full force. The beautiful thought of him pushed all else from her mind. Now she was free to date Woody!

Her brow wrinkled in a frown. But how was she supposed to let him know she was free? As far as he knew, she was still madly in love with some guy from Pittsburgh. What was she supposed to say? "Excuse me, sir, you may be interested to know that I've just dumped my boyfriend so you can ask me to the movies Saturday night if you want." Or, how about a subtle sign taped to her locker. Something like: "No boyfriend, can date. Any interested candidates whose first names start with a 'W' please sign up below."

Kim giggled. No, she'd call him up that very night and ask him to go cycling with her. She'd explain everything then.

Both of her parents were out when she got home, so she headed straight for the phone. At the last second, she hesitated. It had seemed so simple, just to call Woody up, when she'd thought about it on the bus. What made her think he wanted to talk to her, though? Just because she'd ended things with David didn't mean that Woody was chomping at the bit to take up with her. Maybe he was out with Phoebe tonight. Maybe Phoebe was at his house right now. Maybe she should just cool it and wait for him to call her.

Kim argued back and forth with herself.

Wait a minute, she finally thought with a jolt.

Here I am — supposedly the great liberated woman — and I'm standing here quaking in my shoes at the thought of calling a boy. What's the worst he can do? Tell me never to call him again. Big deal!

Kim's firm resolve started to break down as she listened to Woody's phone ring and ring. Oh well, if he's not even home, that solves the problem very easily, thought Kim. But just at that moment the phone was answered. Woody!

"Hello, Woody," said Kim. "It's. . . ."

"Kimberlation," he cried. "I thought you'd gone for the whole weekend!"

"I thought so, too, but things didn't — well, didn't work out."

"What's happening?"

Again Kim's resolve threatened to desert her. "Uh . . . well . . . I was just wondering if you wanted to go for a long bike ride tomorrow. I need the exercise."

"Geez, I'd love to, but I'm supposed to play dutiful son tomorrow," he said. "You know the routine — Mom wants me to hang around for a big pot roast meal, then Dad plans to reinstate slavery by having me rake the yard."

Kim's heart sank. "Oh," she said.

"How about Monday after school, though?" asked Woody enthusiastically.

"Terrific," Kim cried with relief.

"Meet you out by the bikes at three. Okay?"

"Great!"

Kim leapt into the air before the receiver was back in place.

"Yaahooo!" she yelled.

Chapter 6

"Kim, I'm so glad I caught you!" exclaimed Brenda, bouncing up to Kim's locker.

Kim gave the combination lock one more spin before turning around. Brenda was so excited she seemed to be vibrating all over, and her large dark eyes were glowing.

"Okay, okay," said Kim. "Let me guess. You just won the million-dollar lottery and I'm the very first to know. Right?"

Brenda giggled. "Better than that."

"Mr. Barnes gave you an A on that English quiz Friday?"

Brenda giggled again. "I'd have a better chance of winning the lottery. Wrong again. It's Brad."

"He's giving up Princeton to journey to the South Seas with you. You set sail tomorrow."

Kim was in such a good mood, she could have stayed there all day joking with Brenda. They'd never really had a chance to get to know each other. In the few months Kim had been at Kennedy, Brenda had been working out her own problems and Kim had been looking for her little niche in this big, new, exclusive environment. Ever since her visit to Pittsburgh, though, Kim felt more relaxed about everything. Rose Hill was home now. She really felt this for the first time. Kennedy was *her* high school. Brenda was *her* classmate.

"Don't I wish. The South Seas sounds pretty good right now. I wonder when this weather is going to give up playing winter and decide to get into some serious springtime."

"Take heart, the weatherman on my trusty radio told me it was supposed to go up to maybe seventy degrees today. Doesn't that sound practically tropical?"

"Barely. Just barely," said Brenda. She glanced furtively around the hall, then moved closer to Kim. "What I wanted to tell you is that I'm planning a surprise lunch for Brad on Thursday."

"I thought every lunch was a surprise in our lunchroom," joked Kim. She was in such a good mood. Knowing that in just four hours she and Woody would be off together, had her floating on a cloud of happiness. She knew the perfect place to take him.

"That's for sure," said Brenda, laughing. "That's why I'm asking everyone to bring something. Something special. The lunchroom supervisor has already given me permission to put three or four tables together. They were so incredibly nice about this."

"That sounds neat," said Kim. "What's the occasion? Is it his birthday?"

"No, that's in June. We're going to celebrate his acceptance at Princeton. He told me how good everyone's been, listening to him go on and on about this thing for years. I thought it'd be fun to share the moment of triumph."

"But I've only known him a couple of months. . . ." began Kim.

Brenda looked down at the floor, then straight into Kim's eyes. "I want you there. I know how being a new student around this place can be the pits. You've really handled it well. I'm sure everyone considers you part of the crowd now."

Kim didn't know what to say at first. In some ways, she didn't quite like the idea that she'd passed some unspoken, unwritten test that was beyond her control, that she'd been scrutinized and not found lacking, that she was finally accepted by the Kennedy elite. But at the same time she was pleased. She wanted to be part of Kennedy now more than ever.

"That sounds great, Brenda. I'd love to be there. What can I bring?"

"Anything you'd like," said Brenda breathlessly. "I thought about assigning everyone something, but it seemed more fun to go with whatever people came up with."

Kim laughed. "Then you're not going to mind if you have eight salads and a side order of stuffed potato skins?"

"Or maybe eight chocolate cakes and a bag of potato chips."

The girls laughed.

"Want to see what I got Brad?" asked Brenda shyly.

"Sure."

"Taaadaaaa," she said, whipping out a large Princeton sweat shirt for Kim to admire. Looking at the orange shirt with the black tiger on it made Kim realize that their high school days were fast coming to an end. No longer was college just something thought about by the big kids, the one's who'd seemed so old and wise when she'd been a freshman in Pittsburgh. College was what all her classmates had on their minds these days. They *were* the big kids now. Even the thrill of becoming a senior paled occasionally compared to the thought of leaving home for some huge college campus, and deciding what you really wanted to be when you grew up. No more dreams; no more fantasies. It was getting close to the time when major decisions had to be made — decisions that would affect the rest of their lives. Kim even wondered sometimes if cooking was really going to be her life; if she was dedicated enough to make a career of it. Had she closed her mind to other possibilities just because she thought she wanted to be a chef? Her mother was right. Sometimes there were just too many choices, too many decisions to make.

"I have one problem, though," said Brenda, breaking into Kim's thoughts. "I don't know where to keep this until Thursday. Brad always comes by my locker at least once a day. And I want it to be a real surprise."

"Well, he certainly doesn't come by mine,"

said Kim lightly. "How about leaving it here?"

"You sure? It looks like you've got plenty of stuff in there already without cluttering it up with something else," said Brenda, looking into the neat, but crowded, locker. A huge poster on the door showed a black woman staring into a microscope. The caption underneath read: *How do you know the person who finds a cure for cancer won't be female and black?* SUPPORT THE MINORITIES COLLEGE FUND.

"Yeah, well, maybe it'll force me to take some of this junk home," replied Kim. "Really, Brenda, it's no problem."

"Thanks . . . thanks a lot," said Brenda, folding the sweat shirt neatly and putting it back in the bag.

"Here, let me write down my combination for you so you can take it out when you want it."

"That's okay," said Brenda. "My locker's right down there. I see you here all the time. We're bound to cross paths before Thursday."

"I don't know," said Kim. "I've got to get that run-a-thon together — you know, all the posters and stuff. I'd hate not to be here when you need it."

She scribbled down her locker combination on a page in her notebook, then tore it out. "Here. Just be sure you put it exactly on the five. It sticks sometimes."

"Sure. Okay. Thanks a bunch," said Brenda. "Uh . . . oh. Here comes Brad. Quick."

Brenda shoved the package into Kim's locker, then rushed off to meet Brad. His eyes glowed with love as he threw his arms around Brenda.

Kim swallowed hard. She wondered how it felt to love someone so much. She loved her parents probably more than anything in the world. But they never looked at each other like that — like nothing else existed except the little bit of the world immediately around them.

She'd loved her dog, Charlie, too. He was a mongrel, a weird-looking mixture of sheepdog and retriever, but she'd loved him like a member of the family. The day he got run over was the worst day she'd ever lived through. She loved her parents because they were her parents. She'd loved Charlie because he had adored her in return, and needed her so desperately. He couldn't sleep at night if he wasn't sprawled out at the foot of her bed.

But how did it happen? What was it that made people who'd been strangers most of their lives suddenly get to love each other with such intensity? Like Brad and Brenda. How could they be so sure of each other? Did they ever think about breaking up? Most people broke up after awhile. Look at Brad and Phoebe; they'd been dating for two years. And David and her. What had happened there? Was it inevitable that relationships end? If so, what was the point in getting involved in the first place?

Brenda turned and waved at Kim before she and Brad disappeared up the stairs, their arms wrapped around each other.

"So whither are you whisking me off to, fair maiden?" joked Woody.

Kim snapped a clip around the ankle of her

jeans and adjusted her backpack, then looked up at him. He was leaning against his bike in the school lot, his long, slender body completely relaxed, his legs crossed at the ankles. He had on faded jeans and a frayed flannel shirt. A thick band of tape was wrapped around the toes of his sneakers, which were laced in thick neon green.

"I see you dressed for the occasion," said Kim, laughing. The day had turned out as promised, warm and sunny with a soft breeze that wafted smells of spring in the air. Woody rolled up his sleeves. The hair on his arms was dark and curly; his muscles were taut and lean. Kim liked that. She'd never been interested in the Incredible Hulk-type with muscles bulging all over the place. It was too much. No, Woody was just right. Perfect, in fact.

"I'm wounded," said Woody, forcing his face to sag into a mock pout. "I put on my favorite clothes and my best dancing slippers in your honor. I thought you'd be thrilled."

Kim giggled. "Those dancing slippers may have seen one pirouette too many."

"But the laces, the laces. Surely you appreciate a class act when you see it?" begged Woody. "I mean I had to go all the way to Georgetown for these green-os."

"Okay, okay. I'll buy that. The laces can stay," said Kim. "But the shoes . . . well, maybe you could donate them to the Smithsonian. I'm sure they must be famous for something: the sneakers with the most miles ever, maybe? The ugliest shoes in the world — practically prehistoric. Something like that."

"Oh, how you tear my sensitive artist's soul," cried Woody dramatically, then laughed. "Actually, this wardrobe was planned very carefully. Knowing you, I figured we'd be traipsing through alligator-infested rivers or scaling soaring cliffs." He got on his bike and began pedaling off. "Besides, I left my tux at the cleaners."

Kim laughed and cycled after him. As soon as they'd topped the first little hill her muscles warmed up and she felt as though she could ride all day. The wind whisked around her, tossing her wavy hair and fanning her cheeks.

"Okay, so where are you taking me?" repeated Woody when they pulled up at a light.

"To one of my favorite places ever," replied Kim secretively.

"And how have I qualified for this great and rare honor?" asked Woody dramatically.

Kim tried to answer, but nothing came out. Blood rushed to her face. She leaned over and adjusted her ankle clip to keep him from noticing. It had been such a beautiful day and she'd been so excited about being with Woody that she'd forgotten her vow of the night before to tell him about the breakup with David and how she felt about him. Now she didn't feel quite so brave. He might only be interested in her as a friend, and if she opened her big mouth, she'd blow the whole friendship. Was it worth it? The light turned green, and they pedaled off.

"This way," called Kim, turning down a narrow, tree-lined street in the oldest residential section of town. The elite of Rose Hill lived here. The homes were large and gracious with big, rolling lawns hidden by ancient trees. To Kim it seemed like a private hush hung over this section of town, as if it had a secret it didn't wish to share.

It was one of the first places she'd discovered in Rose Hill. All she could do when she first moved here was cycle around trying to figure out her new world. This street had impressed her the most, and the little park at the end was like a fairyland — hidden, exclusive, permanent. She'd come here again and again in those early days. Being the new kid got kind of tough sometimes. And the agony of leaving Pittsburgh and David had been so fresh. The park had wrapped her in its beauty and lessened the hurt. She hoped she wasn't making a mistake bringing Woody here.

"Rosemont Park?" asked Woody when Kim pulled up to the old stone pillars of the entranceway. "I haven't been here in ages. This is neat."

A little ball of tension dissolved in Kim's stomach. She thought he was the kind of person who could appreciate the special decaying beauty of this once vibrant estate, and it was nice to know her guess was correct. When she had first arrived, the people from Welcome Wagon had told her the Thornton estate had been deeded to the town many years ago, on the condition that it always be used as a public park. But most people in town favored the big new Rose Hill Park on the other side of town, because it had a swimming pool and jogging trails, even an outdoor theatre. Rosemont had nothing but its faded beauty and the secrets of its past to offer.

"Seems like you and I are aways arriving at our destination at sunset," said Woody, clamping his lock around their two bikes. "Might be a bad omen — like our relationship is always on the decline."

"Ah, but don't forget," said Kim. "The sun also rises. Right?"

Woody laughed. "Boy, you're quick! Do you like Hemingway?"

"Not much," replied Kim. "To me, he's too macho."

"Because he's always writing about war and male stuff?" asked Woody.

"There's something old Uncle Ernie never mentioned. Women are just as involved in war as men, in different ways," flung back Kim.

"Oh, I don't know about that," said Woody, sinking his hands deep into his pockets.

"Okay," Kim came back. "Name me one great, semi-great, or even mildly interesting female character in a Hemingway novel?"

"Hmmmm . . . that's a toughie. It's been awhile since I read any Hemingway," replied Woody. "Eighth-grade English, I believe."

"Well, you can read him till the cows come home," said Kim, "but I promise you you won't come out cheering for any of his women, or even remember their names. I find books like that unrealistic. There are great men and great women and the one can't exist without the other."

Woody smiled down at her. For a moment they stood looking at each other, and for a second Kim thought Woody was going to hug her. The air between them was charged with its own special electricity.

"Uh, I guess you're right," he said.

"I find relationships between people really fascinating," Kim continued, walking double time to keep up with his long strides.

"Yeah. Me, too."

Somehow it seemed to Kim that there should be more to say on this subject. Maybe this was the right time to bring up her visit with David, but Woody seemed to be off in another world. He was forging ahead, staring at the ground.

"Webster, slow down," said Kim finally. "Your legs are at least twice as long as mine. Save some of that energy for the run-a-thon."

"I'm sorry," said Woody, immediately slowing his pace. "I was thinking."

"This is a good place for thinking, isn't it?" said Kim, quietly linking her arm through his. Woody tensed, but didn't pull away. "When I first came to Rose Hill I used to come here a lot — just to think."

"And what did you think about?"

Kim gave a short laugh. "It all seems so melodramatic now, but I was trying to figure out where I fit into Rose Hill, and why we had to leave Pittsburgh."

"And David?" asked Woody hesitantly.

"Yes," said Kim. "But that's all in the past now."

"Even David?"

"Even David." Kim wished Woody would show some kind of reaction to indicate whether he thought this was good news or bad news. But he just kept walking along, staring at the ground.

This wasn't how she'd imagined it at all. He was supposed to stop, then slowly take her in his arms and tell her that her breakup with David was the best news in the world, that she'd just made his day, his week, his year — his life. Kim was surprised and slightly horrified by her runaway thoughts. She had always laughed at all that mushy stuff.

"Now, I want to show you my favorite place," said Kim, grabbing Woody's arm more firmly. She couldn't stand it. Didn't he feel anything for her? She'd certainly gotten a lot of signals during the time they'd spent together that said he did. She wasn't used to someone taking over her life . . . her thoughts . . . her emotions like this. Especially someone who didn't even know he was doing it. Frustration welled inside her.

Kim led him back through the old rose garden, around the goldfish pond filled with decaying leaves, and into a small pine grove. The needles were thick and damp, and heavy with that wonderful outdoorsy smell. It was so perfect. Kim and Woody inhaled their breaths simultaneously.

"Doesn't it smell divine," sighed Kim, closing her eyes and imagining they were three thousand feet up in the Blue Ridge Mountains looking for a campsite for the night. This was perfect camping weather. Cool enough for a blazing campfire at night, but warm enough for shorts and knee socks during the day.

Kim sighed again. This had to be the most romantic place in the world. Shafts of sunlight filtered through the thick branches spotlighting patches of the forest floor. There were clusters of brightly colored mushrooms, and pale, delicate toadstools on long, slender stems.

"You know," said Woody, breaking into her thoughts, "wouldn't this make the perfect place to stage a Shakespeare play, maybe *A Midsummer Night's Dream*? Can't you just see the sprites running around in these trees?"

Woody rushed around excitedly. "Perfect. Absolutely perfect," he mumbled, then ran over to another tree for a different angle. "Too wonderful." Finally he turned to Kim, completely unaware of her romantic fantasy. "Do you think the trustees of Rosemont would give me permission?"

"Woody Webster. You are the most frustrating person in the world," yelled Kim, charging at him. He dodged lightly out of her way, and playfully rumpled her hair as he did. Kim charged again. This time he ran behind a large pine tree. Kim rushed around one side and then the other, but each time he just escaped her grasp. Finally she caught him off-guard, and grabbed his shirt sleeve. They spun around and around, then fell to the ground, Kim landing on top of Woody. Her face was inches from his. His eyes were shiny and devilish-looking. That sweet, funny smile, which had dominated her thoughts for so many hours, was now miraculously close. Before she even thought about the consequences, Kim felt herself leaning toward Woody. Their mouths met, and his lips were as warm and tender as she had imagined.

Woody couldn't believe it. One minute he was in the middle of staging his best production yet — the next he was flat on his back in the pine needles, Kim next to him, her soft mouth approaching his. The electric current he felt every time he neared the Kennedy stage was just a spark compared to this sensation. He'd dreamed of kissing someone before, had even tried it once with Julie Merkins. But they'd been eleven, and her mother had come up the stairs and put an end to it fast. Julie had moved away before they got a chance to try it again.

In high school he'd become every girl's friend. He'd had crushes on several girls, like Phoebe, but they'd always been involved with other guys. All he got to do was listen to their problems with love and boys, and had actually gotten quite good at giving advice. He had resigned himself to the fact that there was something about him that made girls trust him and want to be close to him — but not too close.

So what was going on with Kim now? Did she really like him or was she just having fun with him? For the moment, Woody didn't debate the question and gave himself up to the feeling of this kiss, Kim, and these magic woods. That was all the reality he needed right then.

He held Kim closer, both arms wrapped tightly around her. Their hearts were so close together, they seemed to beat in one rhythm — one crazy rhythm like Jerry Lee Lewis gone nuts on the piano. Woody inhaled deeply. Kim smelled like the woods — fresh and clean, and wonderfully real.

"Woody," sighed Kim, pulling away and propping herself up on her elbow. "What's happening?"

He looked at her shiny eyes and thick hair, which the sunlight had turned golden. Behind her the pine trees soared to the heavens. The picture before his eyes was almost painful. It was everythink he'd ever wanted — a girl looking at him with love and adoration. Surely he'd wake up in a minute or two, and feel that old, familiar pang of loneliness. He smiled. People always thought Woody Webster was on top of the world, the permanent clown, forever cheerful and laughing. No one saw it was an act, a very clever act to cover the hurt of never having someone special to share his feelings with.

He kissed Kim lightly on the lips and let his breath out with a rush. "I think you better tell me what's going on," he said at last, pushing a strand of hair gently from her eyes.

"I . . . I really want to be with you, Woody," Kim admitted, staring at the buttons of his shirt.

"What about David?"

"I told you. That's over."

"Am I just the lucky guy getting caught on the rebound?"

The minute he said this, Woody wished he could back up and erase his words, just as he could on his tape deck. The hurt in Kim's wide green eyes was real.

"I'm sorry, Kim," he said, squeezing her in tight to his chest. "It's just this all comes as kind of a shock to me. I thought we were friends."

"We are, Woody," said Kim. "That's what's so

neat about it. We were friends first, and now this. I really think you are one of the most wonderful people in the world."

"And I think you're nuts," he said, kissing her cheeks and forehead. "You attacked me."

"Well, I didn't think you'd ever take the hint," she said, running her fingers through his thick tangle of curls. "Anyway, are you complaining?"

"No," he whispered, finding her mouth once again. "Not at all."

This time the kiss was slow and gentle.

"Now tell me what happened in Pittsburgh," said Woody. "Everything."

Kim lay in the crook of his arm, her head on his chest, and told him about her day with David.

"I like David. He's a very nice person, but I don't love him," she concluded, looking up through the pine boughs to the pinks and purples of the late afternoon sky. "Our relationship had been over for a long time. But I realized it this weekend."

"But why me?" asked Woody. "I knew we were buddies, and I must admit I always wanted it to be more, but I've learned my lesson with girls who are involved with other guys. I've been hurt. So, from now on, play it safe and be a friend, not a competitor, I said to myself."

"Why you?" said Kim playfully, rubbing his chin. "Because I think you're kind and gentle, and very smart. And you make me laugh; we always have such fun together."

"Don't stop," joked Woody. "This is starting to sound very good. Now let's get back to the smart and funny bit."

"You've got to earn it," said Kim teasingly, rolling away from him. He immediately pinned her down.

"Oh, Woody, you'll mess up my hair," laughed Kim, sitting up and starting to pick the pine needles off herself.

"Here, let me do that," he said, gently plucking each pine needle as if it were a priceless treasure. Finally, he wrapped her tightly in his arms and rested his chin on her head.

"Kim, I'm still not sure what's happened here today, but you've made me the happiest guy in the world. You have my permission to kidnap me any time you'd like."

Kim kissed his neck, feeling the blood pulsing through his veins. "I will. I promise."

When they kissed this time, Woody felt no hesitation, just a warmth that spread from him to her and back again.

Chapter
7

"How come you're painting them?" asked Shawn, Phoebe's little brother, as he watched his sister slap paint on the shutters of her bedroom. "They look fine to me."

"They look fine to me, too," agreed Phoebe, sinking the paintbrush deep into the pale yellow paint, then wiping the excess off on the lip of the can. "But Mother doesn't think so."

"It's your room. I don't see why you have to do stuff to it, if you don't want to," continued Shawn with the clear logic of a ten-year-old.

For a change, Phoebe was actually glad to have Shawn around. Being grounded for almost one month had given her a different perspective on her little brother's company. Painting the shutters was her last task before all the money for Woody's car was repaid. Saturday would be her first day of freedom. Phoebe stared down at the paint dripping off the brush. Her first day of freedom and nothing to do. She'd probably end up sitting at home as she'd done for the past month. Chris would be out with Ted, Brenda would be with Brad. Sasha and Wes would be desperate to be alone, after a month of stealing kisses in Sasha's parents' store. Life was sure a lot easier when you had a boyfriend, she concluded, catching a gob of paint with her brush as it oozed down the front of the shutter. If only Griffin were here. She wiped away the paint and continued her work. Maybe Woody would like to go to the movies or something.

"You know, I think you ought to make your hair all yellow," said Shawn, breaking into her thoughts. "You look nice with yellow hair."

Phoebe glanced in the mirror. Somehow she'd gotten a patch of paint on the side of her head. She must have leaned into a shutter without knowing it. Throwing down the paintbrush on the stack of newspapers, she stomped into the bathroom to wash her hair, Shawn right on her heels.

"Maybe you should wear a scarf," he suggested, leaning on the side of the sink. "Like Mrs. Beasley does when she works in the garden. Her hair looks perfect all the time."

"I think that has more to do with her can of hairspray than the scarf," said Phoebe patiently.

"Yuck. I'm glad you don't use that junk. I think your hair looks pretty the way it is, kind of loose and floppy."

Phoebe smiled down at Shawn. He had really been making an effort to be nice, as if he sensed things weren't going too well for her these days. Last Saturday he had brought her a cup of coffee as she lay in bed. Sure, it had been only six-thirty in the morning, and the coffee was so strong she could have commanded it to march back to the kitchen on its own two feet. But he'd been so proud of himself as he sat on the end of the bed to watch, she'd drunk the whole thing.

Phoebe wrapped a towel around her head and went back to her painting. One more shutter and she was finished. Her parents definitely had to un-ground her now, thought Phoebe wryly. There was nothing left to do around the house. She'd done it all — scrubbing, painting, window washing, raking.

"You look like an ancient Egyptian with that towel around your head," said Shawn.

"You think so?" said Phoebe absentmindedly.

"Yeah, like Tutankhamen."

"How do you know about Tutankhamen?" asked Phoebe in surprise.

"Oh, I know all about him. Our class went to the Smithsonian last week, to the exhibit about him. It was really great. He was just a kid like me, and he got to be king of Egypt."

"I think they were called pharaohs, weren't they?"

"Yeah, that's the word. Anyway, you knew what I meant, didn't you?"

Phoebe was about to answer when the phone rang shrilly downstairs.

"My favorite brother, would you get that, please?"

Shawn got off her bed reluctantly. "Do you think Tutankhamen's sister ordered him around like this?"

Phoebe laughed and pretended to come after him with the paint brush. Shawn squealed and raced down the stairs.

Phoebe stood back and surveyed her work. She had to admit the shutters looked pretty. Her mother had picked out the color. At first, Phoebe thought it was too bland. She wanted something bolder, something that would make a statement, but it was probably just the mood she was in at the time. Being told she couldn't go anywhere until she'd worked off her share of the repairs to Woody's car had hit hard. Now the pale yellow reflected the sunlight around the room in a halo of soft light. It created a quiet and peaceful atmosphere.

Phoebe sighed. Life sure had changed. A few months before she would have been with Brad after school listening to him worry about getting into Princeton, going over some notes he wanted her to type up for the next student council meeting. They would have wandered arm-in-arm to the sub shop for a snack, then talked on the phone after supper, planning their weekend together.

Then she was lost in the haze that Griffin created: that wonderful, magical haze that had surrounded her and lifted her into a world that was so alive and thrilling. Now she was down to earth again — discussing pharaohs with her little brother and painting shutters. Phoebe laughed.

It was pretty funny when she stopped to think about it.

"Pheeb. It's for you," shouted Shawn up the stairs. "Some lady."

Probably Chris, thought Phoebe, wandering slowly down the stairs. Sometimes these days it was almost painful talking to her best friend. Life was good for Chris. She was so positive, it made Phoebe realize how empty her own life was. Oh, well, she could always tell her about the beautiful shutters. They really did improve her room. Maybe she could talk her mom into a new bedspread, too.

"Ms. Hall?"

The voice was familiar, but Phoebe couldn't quite place it. "Yes," she answered hesitantly.

"Ms. Hall, this is Mr. Solomon's office calling from New York."

Phoebe's heart did a backflip while her tummy burbled with anxiety. "Oh yes, hello." Did she have some news about Griffin? Was he there in the office now? Phoebe's hands shook with impatience.

"I've got some information for you. Not much, but it might help."

Phoebe heard the rattling of paper. She wished she could crawl through the phone line and speed things up.

"Yeah. Here it is. Neill. Griffin. Right?"

"Yes," said Phoebe breathlessly. "Yes, that's the one. Do you know where he is?"

"Yes . . . well . . . no," replied the woman. More papers rattled. "Seems like he did try out for that play. Got called back three times."

A chill ran down her spine. Please let Griffin be all right, she prayed. "But he wasn't in the play when it opened, was he?" asked Phoebe.

"No, no he wasn't," replied the woman. "Strange. . . ."

"What's strange?" Phoebe just knew the woman had bad news. She couldn't think of any other reason Griffin would have cut her off like he did, if something terrible hadn't happened.

"Well, after that, his file ends. We don't have any other record of him trying out for anything. Nothing."

"Is there a phone number or address? Anything?"

"Yeah, there's a phone number. No address. But this file is pretty old now. I doubt if that number's any good. Things change pretty fast in this market. You can try it, I guess. It's a two-one-two area code." Phoebe took down the numbers the woman dictated to her. "Good luck."

"Thanks," said Phoebe. "Thanks for all your help. I really appreciate it."

Phoebe stared at the number until the figures got blurry before her eyes. Now that she had it, she wasn't sure if she wanted to call. She didn't know if she could handle another disappointment. Slowly she dropped the receiver back into its cradle.

Kim rushed over to answer the phone. Her spirits were flying. After a slow beginning, the afternoon with Woody had gone better than she'd ever imagined. Woody really liked her! She could still feel his arms holding her so gently and tenderly. It had been wonderful.

"Hello, Woody!" she exclaimed, when she recognized his voice. Joy overflowed her heart. "Want to go for a midnight walk in Rosemont Park, if you know what I mean?" She laughed at her own joke. There was silence on the other end.

"Woody? You still there?"

"I'll always be here," he said in a quiet voice. "Always."

"What happened? Did you decide I was a better deal than the math quiz you're supposed to be studying for?"

"Kim, don't joke about that," he said seriously. "You know you are the most important thing in the world to me."

"Have you been watching a sad movie or something?" asked Kim, totally confused by Woody's solemn tone. His one-liners usually kept her on her toes, his quick wit was one of the many things she loved about him. But it sounded like he'd lost his best friend.

"No," he sighed. "I was just thinking about us and what a beautiful afternoon we had. I wanted to call and make sure you were real, not something I had dreamed up."

"Well, I'm very real . . . or there's one weird ghost inhabiting my mirror," said Kim flippantly.

"Oh, Kim. I miss you so much it hurts."

Part of Kim was thrilled to know he'd been thinking about her, that he really missed her like that, but part of her didn't recognize this serious person she was talking to. It didn't sound like Woody at all. He sounded like a flat tire.

There was an awkward silence. She could hear Woody breathing, but he didn't say anything.

"Breaker one-oh-nine, this is Fuzz-top calling the Mad Cyclist. Come in MC, if you're out there." Kim imitated all the crackling noises of a CB radio in action.

Woody sighed again. "I just wanted to call to be near you. We could keep our phones off the hook all night and just talk occasionally. That way, we'd always be in touch."

Kim thought he was joking but when he didn't laugh, she stifled her own giggles. She'd never heard anything so crazy in her life. For a joke it was funny — for real, it was ridiculous.

"Actually, if I don't get off this phone and chained to my calculator, I may make history on that math quiz tomorrow — the worst grade ever. So low it won't even be recordable on any instruments known to man."

"Okay. If you've got to go, you've got to go." For a moment Kim thought he was starting to be funny, but it was soon obvious he wasn't. "I'm thinking about you every minute. Know that."

"I'm thinking of you, too, Woody," she said softly. "Good-night."

"Good-night."

Kim shook her head as she replaced the receiver. She couldn't believe the person she'd just spoken to was the light-hearted, happy clown she'd been with all afternoon.

Just thinking of Woody's twinkling eyes and warm smile, though, sent Kim's insides into wonderful, frizzy chaos. David had never had this effect on her. Never. But she couldn't deny it all kind of scared her, too. She always knew what was happening with David. Things were predictable. She had it all under control. Not with Woody. Not at all.

Chapter
8

Kim stared at the stack of cookies cooling on the rack. They didn't look quite right, but then it was a new recipe; maybe they were supposed to come up like that — all lumpy and irregularly shaped. She was too sleepy to brood about it any longer. This was Thursday, the day of Brad's special lunch. She'd been so wrapped up with all her new feelings for Woody she'd almost forgotten. She'd gotten up at five-thirty A.M. to make these cookies. This was no time for her cooking skills to fail.

"Are you certain you don't want me to drive you to school this morning?" asked her mother. "You've got so much to carry — all those cookies *and* your books."

"It's okay, Mom. I can manage." Kim felt that she could handle anything these days. You want the house moved to the other side of the street?

No problem. I'll put it on my back and carry it right on over. Weather not warm enough? Let me order you up a little bit of summer. Pledges were coming in thick and fast for the run-a-thon, and she and Woody were spending every afternoon together. Life couldn't have been better.

"How'd that recipe turn out?" her mother asked, sniffing the plate of cookies. "They certainly smell delicious."

"I don't know," said Kim, packing them into a shoe box. "They look a little strange, don't you think?"

"You mean you haven't tasted them?" her mother asked in surprise.

"To tell you the truth, the recipe came up a bit short," admitted Kim. "I'm not sure there's even enough for everyone at the lunch."

"Oh, don't worry, dear. It always works out. Remember the party at the Fitches? The one I did all those crab pasties for? Well, I thought I'd made more than enough but when I walked in and saw all those people, my heart sank."

"What did you do?" asked Kim. "Call out for pizza to fill in the gap?"

Mrs. Barrie chuckled. "I sure felt like it. But what I did was utter a silent prayer — and someone must have been listening. There were just enough. Even one left over. So don't worry. I'm sure everything will be just fine. I do wish you'd let me drive you, though."

"Oh, Mom. Don't worry," said Kim, kissing her mother on the cheek. "I'll be fine. It's such a beautiful morning, I'd hate myself if I didn't get out in it."

"You know best," her mother smiled. "You are the only one of my children who got endowed with a little common sense. The others take after me, I'm afraid. Run along, then. It's eight-fifteen already." She kissed her daughter and retied her scarf.

Kim thought about her mother as she cycled to school. She felt that she had a definite responsibility to be sure her mother was happy on her own before she graduated from high school. If only Earthly Delights would really take off and become a full-time job, so her mother would have something she really liked to do and would be able to forget the fact that all her children were gone.

Being the youngest in the family had some heavy responsibilities, Kim thought as she sailed down the hill by the big park. Everyone always said the oldest got the raw deal being the one the parents made all their mistakes on. But her position was just as tough, she decided. More than the other two, her mother didn't want to let her go.

At the bottom of the hill the land flattened out, and Kim pedaled at a leisurely pace along the edge of the park. Crocuses were bursting up through the soil: beds of purple and yellow and white. In another week or so, the mountain laurel and rhododendron would be in full bloom. That would be a perfect time to go cycling in the state park, she thought. It had miles of bike trails, and lots of neat places for picnics. Private picnics. A shiver ran up Kim's spine.

When she got to school Kim parked her bike

next to Woody's. She knew it was corny, but it gave her a nice warm feeling during the day to think of their two bicycles out there together, keeping each other company. She could see them from her fifth-period classroom. Somehow, the way they were parked, kind of leaning toward each other, lent them an almost human quality. She could almost imagine them discussing what adventure might be in store for them when their owners came to get them after school.

When she got to her locker, her good mood deflated. There was a note sticking out of the door. She didn't have to guess where it came from. Woody. This would be the fifth note in two days. With her heart racing, she unfolded the paper: "Before you came along, I was a shell without a shore, a wind without a tree, a fish without a stream. You have given me everything, for which I will always be eternally grateful."

Kim let her breath out in a long sigh; her heartbeat returned to normal. She flipped the note over several times in her hand, hoping it would disappear or — better yet — she'd find a big "Ha, Ha" written somewhere. Woody's notes were getting worse and worse . . . mushier and mushier. She just couldn't believe he had written this stuff. Woody *could* write really well; she'd read some of the articles he'd done for the school paper. They were good — really good — witty and satirical, but this was like some bad joke. The trouble was, to Kim, it wasn't the slightest bit funny.

She was about to crumple the note up, but she

got the feeling someone was staring at her. Looking up, she saw Woody leaning against his locker several feet away. She blushed.

"Hi," he said. "Uh . . . you got my note?"

Of course she had. If he'd bother to look, he could see it in her hand, but he was staring into her eyes.

"Did you . . . did you like it?" he asked shyly. "I wanted you to have it first thing this morning, to start your day."

"Yes . . . thank you," replied Kim, feeling very awkward. Just looking at Woody made her go all trembly. She wanted nothing more than to cross those four feet of scuffed green tiles and put her arms around him, to feel his arms around her. That's how she'd really like to start her day.

But Woody hadn't cracked a joke since they were in Rosemont Park. When Kim pictured the two of them walking and cycling and exploring together, it was the old, funny Woody she imagined, not this stranger. Kim was beginning to wish she'd never let him know how she felt. In some ways she felt just being friends with the old Woody would be preferable to trying to make a relationship work with this lovesick puppy standing in front of her. Things weren't going right at all, and she didn't know what to do about it. She only hoped he'd snap out of it soon. Then she remembered how she'd floated around in the early days with David; maybe, she thought to herself, it was just a stage people went through the first time they got involved with someone else.

"I'm going to leave you a note every day,"

declared Woody. "Because every day I want to remind you that I'm thinking of you, to let you know how much I care."

Kim tried to smile, but the smile got stuck.

"That's okay, Woody," she said. "I really appreciate the notes and all, but you could just give me a nice big hug every morning instead. You know, save a tree, hug a friend."

"I can do both," said Woody, hugging her enthusiastically. Kim sighed. He felt so warm and solid.

"Hi, Woody. Hi, Kim." Phoebe gave them a strange look and kept on going.

"Hi, Phoebe," Kim called back, but Phoebe didn't turn around.

"I'm going to walk you to class," said Woody, taking her books from her.

"Woody, that's nuts. You've got chemistry all the way down at the other end of the building." Woody had given her a copy of his schedule the day before, so they could try to meet between classes whenever possible.

"I want to talk to you about something," he said, starting down the hall with her.

Kim shook her head, but didn't argue. Maybe he was going to explain his weird behavior. That she was willing to listen to.

"I've been thinking," he said earnestly, "that I might make a good chef. What do you think?"

"I think you hate to cook and it's a dumb idea," said Kim in exasperation. "You're a brilliant stage manager. Why in the world would you want to give that up?"

"I want to share what you're doing," he said.

"I can't stand the thought of our being apart. So if I learn to cook I could help you and your mom out, and we could have more time together. Good idea?"

"Definitely a bad idea," said Kim. Then, noticing the hurt in his face, she softened her tone. "Woody, I love what you do, and I'm glad you like what I do. I think that's very important to a relationship — to respect each other's work — to give each other space to breath in. We can't spend every minute together."

"I don't see why not," said Woody moodily. "Or maybe you just don't feel as strongly about me as I do about you."

"Woody, could we save this discussion for lunch? The bell is going to ring in exactly three seconds, and I don't want to be late to class."

Woody left her reluctantly. Kim watched him amble down the hall. Was she making a big mistake talking to him like that? It was obvious he wanted something more from their relationship, but she wasn't sure exactly what or why. He was acting so strangely these days. Why couldn't he back off a bit, cut out the mushy notes and the puppy-dog devotion? But maybe she was wrong. She hoped she wasn't trying to make him into another David, all efficient and aloof. Maybe David really was her type. She sure didn't seem to be handling Woody's brand of ultra-romanticism very well.

"Sorry I'm late," said Kim, slipping into a seat at the long table in the lunchroom. "I had to photocopy some more run-a-thon forms. They're going like hot cakes." She glanced down the table, before putting down her box of cookies. There was all sorts of delicious-looking food: fried chicken, a tuna casserole, and even baked apples. It was an impressive turnout. Woody filled a plate and put it in front of her. Kim smiled her thanks, even though she would have preferred to choose her own meal.

"Now that everyone's here," said Brenda, standing up, "I'd like to give Brad his present." Shyly she reached under her chair and pulled out the package that had sat in Kim's locker. Kim joined in the laughter and applause when the wrapping fell away, and Brad held up the Princeton sweat shirt. His face beamed with happiness and pride. Without hesitating, he took Brenda in his arms and held her tight. A big cheer arose. Woody squeezed Kim's hand under the table.

"Well . . ." began Brad, facing the assembled crew. "I'm not very good at speeches."

Kim laughed with the rest. As student body president, Brad had to give at least one speech a week.

"But I think this occasion calls for a try, at least," he continued.

"Keep it short, Davidson," shouted Ted jokingly.

Kim could feel the table vibrating from the clapping and stomping around her. Ted was performing a drum solo on the table with his fork and knife, making Sasha's pencil collection hop around crazily.

"I just want to thank everyone for being so supportive of my efforts to get into Princeton."

"We're just happy to get rid of you," said Ted. "We thought you'd never get out of here."

Brad laughed. "Well, you clowns had better come visit me next year. I know I'm the first one to leave this group, but I want you to know I'll be taking part of each of you with me. You guys are great. Thanks a lot."

Brenda was the first one on her feet. A standing ovation. Soon, even the people sitting in the far corners of the cafeteria, without a clue to what was going on, were on their feet yelling and stomping. Finally, things settled down. Kim offered her cookies around.

"It's a new recipe, so I can't vouch for them," she said, passing the box down the table.

"I'm sure they're going to be sensational," broke in Woody.

"Don't speak too soon," said Ted, trying to make an inroad into his cookie. "I'm afraid what we have here is a cleverly disguised hockey puck." He dropped it on the table. It landed with a hard thunk. "This could cause a revolution in the National Hockey League . . . and a lot of injuries."

"Here, here," broke in Brad, staring intently at his cookie. "How insensitive you are. Kim has introduced us to a new form of life — Moonstonius Far-Outus — and you're making fun of it." Kim groaned through her laughter. Making cookies at five-thirty in the morning was definitely not a good idea.

"Sorry, guys," she said. "Guess that'll teach me not to use you all as guinea pigs, huh?"

"I think they're delicious," said Woody, forcing himself to get through one of them and starting on another. Kim couldn't believe his teeth didn't fall out. These cookies were hard. No moist and chewy here. She sided with Ted. They would make great hockey pucks if the NHL didn't rule them out as lethal. Woody ground through another one.

"Woody, don't be a nut," said Kim. "These cookies are disgusting, even I admit it. You're not going to hurt my feelings by not eating them, I promise. I'd rather you threw them away than sue me for all the dental work you're going to have done." She laughed with the others, but Woody kept right on crunching.

"Well, hello everyone. No one told me they were filming *Animal House* right here in our own little school," said Laurie Bennington, wandering up with Lars in tow. She looked disdainfully down the long, messy table. She had her arm tucked through Lars'. "Did you have a nice lunch?"

"Ah, Laurie," said Ted. "It's good to see you."

"It is?" Laurie asked.

"Of course." Ted's eyes twinkled mischievously. "Here, have a cookie."

Laurie took the cookie he offered and tried to bite into it. Chris started to giggle. Laurie's expression didn't change.

"It's divine. Absolutely divine. You must give me the recipe, Ted. They're a credit to your culinary abilities."

With that she sauntered off still attached to Lars, who hadn't picked up any of the subtle jabs.

Kim watched them leave. She had to give Laurie credit. She'd never seen that girl blush, or look anything but controlled and in command. Laurie heard what she wanted to hear and the rest rolled off. She was amazing.

"Poor old Lars is sure going to go home with a strange view of American girls," said Sasha.

"Whew, you're not kidding," said Ted.

"I wonder if she'll give away all those Scandinavian clothes when he leaves," said Phoebe. "I can't believe how her look has changed."

"I must admit, I preferred the exposed shoulder to the bulky-knit look," teased Brad, parrying a playful punch from Brenda. He kissed her captured hand, and she smiled back at him adoringly.

"I just can't believe how she could mold herself into someone else like that," called Chris. "It's like she doesn't have a mind of her own anymore."

Kim glanced at Woody. He was staring intently at her as if they were completely alone, his big dark eyes overflowing with love. Kim looked away quickly, embarrassed by this obvious show.

Woody's going the same route as Laurie, thought Kim. He's losing himself in me, and that's exactly what I don't want. It's not healthy. It's going to ruin a great relationship. She shook her head in frustration. Woody squeezed her hand.

Chapter
9

"So what's going on with you and Kim?" asked Phoebe, settling down in the booth and plunging her spoon into her hot fudge sundae. It was Friday, her first night of freedom, and as she had feared, by five o'clock the evening had loomed before her, long and lonely. She'd sat in her newly painted room watching the shadow of the huge oak tree out front get longer and longer until it dwarfed the tree itself.

Funny how life went on without you, she had mused, resting her head on the window sill. Four months earlier she was involved with the follies, breaking up with Brad and falling in love with Griffin; she'd been an important part of many groups. Her life revolved around school and all the many activities there. She and Chris were always at each other's houses or on the phone. And even after she'd been grounded, at least her friends had called and stopped by. But then she'd gotten too busy with all the chores to spend much time just hanging out.

Chris still called about once a week, but it was like they were in different worlds right now. She was so wrapped up in school and Ted, Phoebe found herself getting to know the insides of her house and her little brother's mind as never before.

Phoebe glanced around the ice-cream parlor as though she were seeing it for the first time. She'd chosen it because she knew most of the gang would be at the sub shop. She wanted to be alone with Woody. They hadn't had one of their good talk sessions in ages. She'd missed Woody — he always saw things so clearly.

"Huh?" replied Woody absentmindedly.

"I said, what's happening with you and Kim? From the look of things you've finally broken your own rule about not dating a girl who's involved with someone else."

"She's not involved with anyone else," said Woody defensively. "Things are over with that guy in Pittsburgh."

"Then why aren't you out with her tonight?" asked Phoebe, pulling her hair back before it fell into her sundae.

"She and her mom had to cater a dinner at Senator Fitch's house," said Woody mournfully.

Phoebe stared at his woebegone face with mixed feelings. When she and Woody had been together before, she had had his complete attention, and he was always able to pull her out of the worst funk. Tonight he was distracted; he hardly seemed to notice her at all. He'd even

111

been uptight at the movie they'd just gone to. Phoebe had laughed till tears rolled down her cheeks, and it felt great, but Woody had complained that the movie had obviously been made on a tight budget. He was in such a bad mood, she almost wished she hadn't asked him out.

"Is it serious?" asked Phoebe.

"What? Oh, you mean with Kim?"

"No, I mean you and that milkshake. The way you're staring at it, it looks like you might be about to ask it to go steady." Phoebe giggled. Woody sighed.

"It's her favorite kind," he said quietly.

"Who's favorite what?" asked Phoebe, completely confused.

"Kim's. The milkshake. She loves strawberry milkshakes."

Phoebe rolled her eyes. "Boy, have you got it bad. I thought I had gone to pieces over Griffin, but I think you're setting a new record for soppiness."

Woody looked up suddenly and intently. He grabbed Phoebe's hands in his. "I love her, Phoebe. I love Kim. She's the most wonderful thing that's ever happened to me."

Phoebe had to glance away. His look was too intense. Woody Webster had finally gone over the brink. Love had struck and left him totally defenseless. Phoebe knew how he felt, though. The same thing had happened to her when Griffin walked into her life. But, seeing Woody like this, she had to admit that she felt a twinge of jealousy. After all, she'd been number one in

Woody's life for so long. Now she was losing him, too.

"I'm so glad for you, Woody," she said, trying to smile. And she *was* happy for him, even though she couldn't deny the feeling of loss she had, too. "Being in love can be the most wonderful thing in the world; it can make you feel like you have no more problems. But then it can be so painful, too."

"Right now, I'm just into the happiness bit," bubbled Woody.

Phoebe looked at her friend. His face was sparkling with happiness. But something was different, too. His eyes, though glowing, had a distracted look, like he was looking at something far away. And come to think of it, she reflected, he hadn't cracked one joke all evening. Not even the funny movie had gotten him going. She sure hoped Woody wasn't in over his head.

"I called that agent in New York," said Phoebe, trying to change the subject. She had the feeling that Woody was going to self-destruct if he kept up this intensity about Kim.

"What agent? Are you going to New York?"

"Geez, Woody, snap out of it. This is your old friend Phoebe. Remember me? Since sixth grade — good buddies and all that? I feel like I've got to make an appointment with your mind in order to have a decent conversation with you."

"Yeah. I guess you're right. I have been kind of out of it lately." He pushed the empty milkshake glass away from him. "Okay. I remember. Griffin's agent. What happened?"

"Not much the first time. But then the woman called me back and gave me a number. She said it was an old number and probably wouldn't do me any good."

"And?"

"And what?"

"What happened when you called? Was he there?"

Phoebe hung her head. "I haven't tried it yet."

"You what!" cried Woody. "What are you waiting for?"

Phoebe realized she didn't have a very good reply. Why had she hesitated so long? The number had been stuck in her dresser mirror for almost four days.

"I don't know. I really don't. Maybe I'm scared he'll reject me again. Right now I can sort of pretend anything I want to is true, but if I call and he tells me to take a hike, then that's it, right? That's the end. I'm not sure if I'm ready for that."

"Pheeb," said Woody with concern, "not knowing is destroying you, too. You haven't been your old self since that guy left. You can't keep going around in this nowhere world, not knowing where he is, hoping he'll come back. You owe yourself some answers."

Phoebe looked up at Woody. He almost seemed like the old Woody again: tousled hair; warm, dark eyes; her friend. He did care. She could see it in his face.

"Yeah, I guess you're right," she said. "But what if he tells me to get lost?"

"What if he does? It's just something you'll

have to deal with," he said, then added more gently, "At least you'll be able to start moving forward again. You're one of the most popular girls at school. I bet there are tons of guys who'd love to ask you out. Come on, Pheeb, give yourself a chance. Call him. See what happens, and take it from there."

Phoebe took Woody's hands. "Thank you," she said quietly. "You're right. As usual. I'll let you know what happens." She smiled warmly and felt renewed energy flood her body. A flicker of her old positive self crept to the surface.

"Wow," breathed Kim when her mother pulled the station wagon into the drive of The Cliff House, the senator's family estate on the banks of the Potomac. "This place is huge."

"Wait till you see the inside," said her mother, easing the car slowly up the long, tree-lined drive. "It's right out of *Gone With the Wind*."

They swung into the side drive marked SERVICE ENTRANCE and pulled up to the kitchen door. The house was ablaze with light.

"I hope we have everything," said her mother, opening up the back of the car and handing boxes out to Kim.

"I'm sure we have," said Kim, although her stomach was doing some heavy churning. This was the biggest event they'd ever handled — a sit-down dinner for forty people. The logistics of getting everything to the table warm and on time boggled her mind. She was glad her mother seemed cool, calm, and collected.

"Oh, Mrs. Barrie. There you are," said Mrs.

Fitch, fluttering up to them. "I didn't think you were going to make it in time. You're a little late, you know."

Kim glanced at the clock on the kitchen wall. Five after six. They were five minutes late! She caught her mother's glance and rolled her eyes. Her mother had warned her about Mrs. Fitch. Nothing was ever quite perfect enough for her.

When she showed them into the dining room, Kim saw how perfect her world really was. A mahogany table, gleaming from the polishings of many generations, stretched from one end of the long room to the other. The silver and crystal it was laid with caught the light from the immense chandelier overhead and tossed it to the four corners of the high ceiling. Bowls of beautifully arranged fresh flowers punctuated the settings, and the linen cloth and napkins were of a heavy, expensive quality with Mrs. Fitch's monogram embroidered on each. A perfectly laid fire awaited a match in the huge stone fireplace. Kim's stomach churned again. She wished now she'd accepted the sandwich her mother had offered her before leaving.

"This is where we'll all be," said Mrs. Fitch, bustling around, poking a flower back in place, straightening a napkin, fussing over the chairs. "Of course I'll be at the head here, with the senator at the other end. The lady to his left, Mrs. Fitzwilliam, is the guest-of-honor, so please do remember to serve her first. The usual order — the pâté, then soup, the main entrée, salad, and finally dessert. Did you manage to come up with something terribly exotic for dessert, as I asked?"

"Of course, Mrs. Fitch, Earthly Delight is known for its desserts," replied Mrs. Barrie calmly.

Kim almost burst out laughing, remembering the cookies she had served at Brad's lunch. She was sure famous for her desserts. Ted and Brad were still teasing her about them.

"Now then . . . have I forgotten anything?" asked Mrs. Fitch, looking nervously around the room. "Oh, yes. Could you light the fire about ten to eight, just before the guests arrive?"

Mrs. Barrie looked the senator's wife straight in the eye. "Mrs. Fitch, I should think it would be more appropriate for you to have one of your servants do that. My daughter and I will have plenty to do in the kitchen."

Way to go, Mom, thought Kim, with a shiver of pride. Mrs. Fitch was ordering them around like a couple of amateurs.

Mrs. Fitch's face got bright red, and her perfectly peroxided curls shook. Uh oh, thought Kim. She's going to kick us out. We've just blown our first big dinner.

"Well . . . yes . . . I suppose that would be best," sputtered Mrs. Fitch. "Now I absolutely must go up and dress. Lilly ran my bath fifteen minutes ago. It's probably cold by now." Kim got the feeling she was trying to blame them for the tepid water, too.

"Well, what did I tell you?" said Mrs. Barrie when they were alone in the kitchen. "Is she a tyrant or what?"

"I vote for the 'or what,'" joked Kim, pulling things out of the bags. She and her mother had been hard at work since eight o'clock that morning. "If I ever complain about you again, Mom, just threaten to sell me to Mrs. Fitch."

"You mean you wouldn't give anything to live in this house?" said her mother with a sly smile.

"If I could make Mrs. Fitch light the fire, I'd probably love it." They both laughed, then worked silently. By eight forty-five everything was in order: the soup, a thin consommé with sherry, was on simmer; salads were all laid out on individual plates, and the rack of lamb was in the oven. Kim and her mother sank down on a couple of stools to await the appointed hour to begin serving.

At that moment Mrs. Fitch rushed in. A gold lamé hostess gown was draped over her ample body, and her curls dropped in heavy bunches about her shoulders. Kim remembered a picture from her Greek mythology book — the goddess Athena striding into battle. That's exactly what Mrs. Fitch looked like. Really quite regal in a puffed-up sort of way.

"Oh . . ." she said, staring at the two seated figures before her as if they were committing some unpardonable crime. "Everything's ready, I presume?"

"Everything," assured Kim's mother.

"I'll ring the bell when I want the first course served. Are we clear on that?" Kim ground her teeth to keep from throwing the mint sauce in Mrs. Fitch's face. Again her mother came to the rescue.

"Quite clear," she said with supreme control.

All at once, Mrs. Fitch's face drained of color.

She stepped closer to the kitchen table and stared down at the salads. Even Mrs. Barrie looked worried now.

"Is something wrong, Mrs. Fitch?" she asked, clasping and unclasping her hands.

"Something is terribly wrong. No, let me rephrase that — something is completely unacceptable." The fat curls were shaking again. Kim went to stand by her mother's side for support. "Do you call this a salad?"

"Most certainly," replied Mrs. Barrie. "What would you call it?"

"A disgrace. Watercress is something cows eat."

"Mrs. Fitch, I assure you, watercress is very much in vogue now," said Mrs. Barrie, obviously in control again. "Why, just last month *Gourmet* magazine devoted their whole issue to watercress."

Mrs. Fitch stared at her intently, but Kim could see that the fire was cooling.

"*Gourmet* magazine, you say?"

"Yes, and *Bon Appetit* the month before. I assure you, it's *the* thing to serve nowadays. Trust me."

Mrs. Fitch stared down at the salads one more time, then turned and stalked out of the room. Mrs. Barrie sank back on the stool.

"Good job, Mom," said Kim, putting her arm around her mother's shoulders. "You handled that like a real pro. You know, you really would have made a great lawyer. It's in your blood. I can tell."

Mrs. Barrie laughed. "Because I talked Mrs. Fitch out of feeding the watercress to the cows?"

"That and other things. You're just pretty cool."

"Thank you dear, but I don't feel the least bit cool right now. Mrs. Fitch is what I call trial by fire."

"Well, look at it this way: If we can survive her, we can survive anything."

"Oh, don't let her get to you," said her mother sweetly. "She's not worth it."

From the first tinkle of the little silver bell at Mrs. Fitch's elbow till the last plate had been brought back into the kitchen and washed, Kim and her mother worked like demons. Finally, the kitchen was all back in order and Kim was packing up the last few things to take home. She wondered how Mrs. Fitch would rate the evening. A success? She couldn't imagine getting any praise from that woman. She kept waiting for her to storm into the kitchen with a list of complaints. But when she did come in, she was actually smiling. She crossed to Kim's mother and shook her hand. Kim and her mother stared open-mouthed with surprise.

"Oh, Mrs. Barrie. Kim. I can't tell you how wonderful your dinner was. I can't thank you enough. That lamb was perfectly cooked and absolutely divine. What did you do to it?"

"I had it in a light marinade overnight," Kim's mother replied, her face starting to glow.

"Well, I tell you, I've had rack of lamb any number of times, but that was the best. Mrs. Fitzwilliam said so, too, and the senator. Lamb is his favorite, and he does get put out when it's overcooked — as it mostly is. And that salad — you were one hundred percent correct. The watercress was the perfect accompaniment."

Kim was pleased the evening had been a success. She was also exhausted and wished Mrs. Fitch would just wind things up with a hasty goodnight and let them go home.

"Now, then, before you go, I understand you do dinners for the freezer? Am I correct?"

"Oh, yes," said Kim's mother. "One of our specialties. They come in regular or low-calorie."

"Well, may I order twenty of your best low-calorie menus? No, make that thirty of the regular." She winked at Mrs. Barrie as if they were old friends. Kim shook her head. Four hours ago, the woman would have been happy to serve up their heads in the soup. Now she was cracking jokes as if they all belonged to the same country club. She could sure change acts fast — like Woody. He'd been heartbroken when she'd told him she couldn't go out with him that weekend. Today was the Fitch party, and tomorrow her grandparents were coming through on their way up from Florida to their summer home in Massachusetts. Kim's dad was taking them all out for a meal to celebrate the first successful dinner party by Earthly Delights.

Kim was pleased that her dad supported their project. It was true he didn't want to get involved, but he did everything he could to let them know he was proud of them — like the stained glass sign in the kitchen. Kim knew it meant a lot to her mother to have his approval. Working in

Washington as he did, they didn't see very much of him, so his little gestures counted for a lot.

Again Kim thought of Woody. That's what he was always trying to do — seek her approval for every move he made. He couldn't accept the fact Kim wanted to be with him just because of *him*, of who he was.

"Okay, dear. Let's call it a night. We've earned the rest," said Mrs. Barrie, turning off the kitchen lights and leading the way out into the dark.

The clock in the car dashboard read one-ten. To Kim it felt more like four A.M.

"Oh my goodness, what's this?" exclaimed Kim's mother as she put her key in the back door of the house. "Something's ripping my stockings." She pushed the door in and switched on the light. A bouquet of long-stemmed red roses was propped up against the wall. "They're for you, dear. How exciting!" Her mother handed her the note.

Kim immediately recognized Woody's handwriting. Her heart pounded. She'd never been sent roses before. In fact, the only flowers she'd ever gotten were the daisies her father sent her when she'd turned thirteen. She laid the note on the counter and arranged the flowers in a simple, white vase.

"Oooh, my, aren't they beautiful," sighed her mother. "Simply beautiful."

"Woody sent them," explained Kim, knowing her mother was dying of curiosity.

"How awfully sweet. They must have cost a fortune, though. Does he have a part-time job?"

"No," said Kim. How could she explain to her mother that Woody would sell the shirt off his back for her if he had to?

"Good-night, Mom," said Kim, taking the roses and note and heading upstairs. "I think you did a great job tonight. A real bang-up job."

"*We* did, dear. *We* did. Thanks for all your help."

Kim lay back on her bed and slowly unfolded the note. *These roses are only a token of my feeling for you. Their beauty pales in comparison to yours. Every hour we're apart I miss you more and more. Think of me tonight as I will be thinking of you. With love, Woody.*

Oh, no, Kim mumbled to herself, feeling instantly deflated. What in the world is going on here? It must be me — I've ruined him. He was such a neat person before he got serious about me. Now he's a mush-heap. Anger and sadness battled heatedly inside her; first one taking over, then the other. She threw the note on the floor and fell sound asleep fully dressed.

Chapter
10

Phoebe woke up long before the sun Saturday morning, her resolve to call Griffin weakening as the day got lighter and lighter. She tried to fall back asleep, to escape her decision, but she couldn't. Her heart pounded uncontrollably at the thought of dialing those ten numbers. She rolled over and pulled the pillow over her head. Why had she let Woody talk her into calling? She flopped over on her back and stared at the ceiling, the familiar pattern of tiny cracks swimming before her eyes. But Woody was right. What was her life going to be like if she didn't call? Miserable, utterly miserable, knowing she'd had a chance to get in touch with Griffin and blown it. And if she did call? Possibly even more miserable. But possibly not.

She rolled on her side to peer at her clock. Only eight. That was a little early to be waking people up on a weekend. She'd have to wait until at least nine. A whole hour. She got up, put on her robe, and wandered downstairs. It was a beautiful spring morning, warm and fresh. She took her cup of coffee into the backyard and sat down on a bench. For the first time that year, she noticed that the birds had returned. The big maples at the end of the lawn were filled with their chattering noises. Sometimes a new flock would fly in, and the noise was almost deafening. And then as each little sparrow or finch found a limb, things would settle down again.

Actually the birds had probably been back for weeks but she hadn't even noticed — usually at this hour she was rushing around getting ready for school, or still asleep on the weekends. Now she felt that she and the birds had the whole world to themselves for just a little while. There was little other movement or noise on this lazy spring morning.

Phoebe sipped her coffee, feeling the warmth of the liquid all the way down to her toes. They were a bit chilly from the dewy grass. She wiggled them, watching the droplets of water roll off. Griffin would love it here right now, she mused. This was exactly his kind of place — quiet and magical, filled with natural wonders: the birds, the spider webs glistening with dew, the honk of a lone goose flying overhead as it sought out its summer quarters. Phoebe vowed to get up earlier in the morning now that spring had come. Maybe she'd even cycle to school or walk from now on.

Eight-thirty. Phoebe went inside and made another cup of coffee. She could hear the television going in the den and knew that Shawn was up, getting his weekly fix of cartoons. She smiled. Life was so simple for a ten-year-old. His biggest concern of the day would be if he were getting good reception on the TV or not. He didn't question whether he was loved, what his future would be, or if his friends still liked him. Phoebe envied him in a way, but finally decided she preferred to be sixteen. The lows could be pretty low, but the highs had been so high.

Her parents stirred in the room above. She would take them a cup of coffee and the paper. No one had done that for them in ages.

She collected the paper and delivered it with her parents' coffee; then she took Griffin's number down from her dresser and shut herself in her father's office. Finally the big hand of the den clock ended its agonizingly slow march to the twelve, and seemed to hover there, reminding her that the appointed hour had arrived — the hour when she'd chosen to call Griffin. At ten past nine, she still hadn't touched the phone, but sat staring at it as if she expected it to jump up and bite her head off, or maybe just miraculously disappear so she wouldn't have to call.

She took a deep breath, spread the sheet with the number on it out on the table, and lifted the receiver. She pushed the numbers slowly, then, halfway through, began again. She wasn't sure if she'd hit the five or the six. The ring was answered almost immediately.

"Photo studio," said a bored voice.

"Uh . . . yes," began Phoebe.

"Can I help you?" The voice was edged with impatience.

"Yes . . . you can . . . I . . . " begged Phoebe. "I want to speak to Griffin Neill, please." The last part came out in a rush. Phoebe wasn't sure she'd made herself understood. No one seemed to be on the other end of the line. Did the person just walk away? Was he coming back? Did he know Griffin? Finally she heard footsteps echoing hollowly on a floor, like someone walking over the gym floor in clogs. They were coming closer.

"Hello." Griffin! Phoebe couldn't believe it. His voice sounded so familiar, so good, still so rich and warm. Tears began an involuntary parade down her cheeks. She couldn't help it.

"Gr — Griffin. It's me. Phoebe." This wasn't at all what she'd planned to say, but it was all that would come out.

"Phoebe! Wow! It's so good to hear you."

Phoebe's heart almost burst with love. "It's so good to hear you, too. Griffin, I've been going crazy not knowing where you were."

"Oh, sweetheart. I'm sorry. I don't want you to be upset. I miss you so much. How's everything?"

"Well, considering I just got off being grounded yesterday, just fine." She told him the story of Sasha and Wes and the cabin and Woody's car. By the end they were both laughing. It felt so good to laugh with Griffin. It seemed so natural to be talking with him. It was so easy. Like they still lived in the same town and were calling each other about their plans for the day. Phoebe couldn't believe she'd agonized so long about this call. It was obviously the right thing to do.

"Ah, Pheeb, you make me miss old Rose Hill,"

127

he said finally. "New York is a whole different scene. There are some real wackos up here."

"Is your work going well?" asked Phoebe, her confidence growing every moment they talked. "Is it working out like you hoped? I'd love to come up and see you in something."

There was a second's silence. "Maybe one day, but not now. Things are too crazy." His voice sounded weird, strained.

"What happened with that play you auditioned for? Did you decide not to do it?" Somehow Phoebe knew she was beginning to ask dangerous questions, but she was starved for information, trying to make up for four months of silence.

"Hey, look, Pheeb. I really appreciate your calling. It's been great talking to you, but I gotta go. Okay?"

"Oh Griffin, I just need to talk for a few more minutes."

"I'll give you a ring next week, maybe. I really do have to run. Bye, Pheeb."

The phone went dead, its lifeless buzz boring its way into Phoebe's soul. She leaned back in her father's big recliner and let its padded leather upholstery wrap around her. She felt as if a ton of bricks had just fallen on her. Her hands were shaking, and her breath came and went painfully.

He'd sounded so positive at first, as though he was really pleased she'd called. Then he couldn't get off the phone fast enough. If that phone call was supposed to solve the dilemma that had been plaguing her, it had been a complete failure. Phoebe's mind reeled with confusion, hurt, and anger. Throwing on her clothes, she left a note for her parents that she was going to Chris's, and stalked out. She had to talk to someone before she exploded into a million pieces.

The first thing that caught Kim's eye when she awoke that morning was the beautiful bouquet of roses shimmering in the sun. They really were so lovely, and they made her feel special. But just for a second. Then the memory of the mushy note came crashing in and destroyed everything. Kim sat up and looked ruefully down at her still-clothed body. She felt rumpled and dirty, and out of sorts, but the bright yellow sun streaming through her window beckoned. Her grandparents weren't due until noon. Why not get in a nice, long bike ride before then? That thought immediately lightened her mood. She leapt into the shower, then chalked a note for her parents on the board in the kitchen, and slipped out into the new day.

Kim hesitated before getting on her bike. Should she call Woody and invite him to come with her? This was his kind of day. He'd love the adventure of an early morning ride. The streets were always so deserted before about ten-thirty on the weekend. They'd have the town to themselves.

The thought of the old Woody weaving in and out of traffic, his red suspenders flashing way ahead of her, his green shoelaces spinning madly around, brought a lump to her throat. She loved the old Woody. She missed him. The new Woody totally confused her. And, she concluded, she wasn't in the mood for more confusion. Today she would cycle by herself and just enjoy the world; take the time to try to figure out what to do about their relationship.

After five minutes, Kim took off her sweat shirt and let the sun beat down on her bare arms. Winter seemed to be finally over. Monday would be a great day for the run-a-thon. She had sixth period free to get everything ready on the track. There was still a lot to do: water stations to set up, monitors to organize, refreshment stands to get in place. And, to judge from the number of entry forms she'd received, there were going to be a lot of runners, which meant a lot of work.

But Kim was excited about it all. She felt certain they would be able to earn what they needed to keep the girls' track team going for another season. Maybe the run-a-thon would become an annual event. It could be used to aid whatever club at school needed it the most that year. With luck, this year's event would convince the authorities that Kennedy was serious about its girls' team, so they would cough up the approprivate funds next year. This was her first real contribution to her new school. She wanted everything to go perfectly.

Kim followed the Potomac for several miles. The river was beautiful — wide and slow, with an occasional patch of white water to let you know it was still able to rock and roll if it wanted to.

Kim stopped at the lookout over the old Indian fish trap — two lines of rocks coming from either bank to form a V in the middle. The Indians used to place a wide-weave basket in the narrow end, and the fish would get swept in by the current and trapped.

Her eyes took in the thick foliage that came right down to the water's edge. She felt if she stared long enough she would be able to make out an Indian or two stalking down the bank, maybe even one pushing a canoe in the river and paddling off. The Potomac always struck her this way, like a time machine that could take her back to pre-Colonial days. It must have been awfully beautiful back then — no pollution, no harsh engine noises. Sometimes Kim felt she had more in common with that world than the one she awoke to every day.

She turned inland and headed back toward Rose Hill. When she passed the gates to Rosemont Park, she suddenly had the urge to turn in, to go back to the magic wood. That's where she'd found Woody and that's where she'd begun to lose him, too. Maybe it held the answers to some of her questions.

She hadn't brought her lock, so she hid her bike in the tangle of rhododendron bushes by the front gate. The buds were heavy, on the brink of bursting into full bloom. Kim couldn't wait. Spring always filled her with a sense of hope and new beginnings.

Walking along the muddy driveway, Kim almost wished she could turn the clock back seven days. If she'd known what was going to happen to Woody, she never would have let him know how she felt. But she remembered the intensity of her desire to be close to him and knew that even if she could go back in time, she'd do the same thing all over again. That afternoon had been the best in her life.

Kim stopped. What was that? That funny, muffled noise? Over in the rose garden. She approached slowly. Peeking through the hedge she saw a girl seated on the old wrought-iron bench, head in her hands, sobs shaking her whole body. Phoebe!

Kim was thrown into immediate turmoil about what to do. She didn't really know Phoebe. But she couldn't ignore the sadness before her. Still uncertain if she was doing the right thing, she walked over to the bench and sat down.

"Phoebe?" she said quietly.

Phoebe looked up. Her bloodshot eyes registered confusion, then suspicion. Kim began to think she'd made a mistake coming over. Maybe Phoebe really wanted to be alone.

"What's wrong?" she asked, giving it one more try. "You look like you just lost your best friend." This sounded so corny, but she didn't know what else to say, and it was true. That's exactly how Phoebe looked. Utterly miserable.

"What are you doing here?" asked Phoebe, taking a deep breath.

"I was just cycling around and decided to come in for a walk. I love this little park."

Phoebe looked around. Kim followed her eyes. New growth shoots were popping out all over the rose bushes. They were badly in need of a trim, but somehow their wildness added to the charm and privacy of this place.

"It's always been one of my favorite places, too," said Phoebe quietly. "We used to come here when I was a little girl. For picnics. I used to pretend that this was my very own estate, that I was the lost heiress and one day someone would knock at my parents' house and tell me the good news."

Kim laughed softly. "I used to think the same thing about the Carnegie Estate in Pittsburgh. Our school went there on a field trip once, and I must have dreamt about that place for months afterward. I decided I'd been born a Carnegie, but since I was just a little girl, and the family had wanted an heir — a boy — they put me up for adoption and that's how my current parents got me."

Phoebe smiled. Not a big smile, but at least a smile. "I've never told anybody my fantasy about Rosemont," she sighed.

"No one knows about my Carnegie dream either. Can you imagine? People would think we were nuts."

They giggled secretively.

"Kim," said Phoebe suddenly, becoming serious. "What would you do if you loved someone very much and you thought they loved you, too, but they kept acting really weird — like one minute they love you, the next they don't?"

Kim tensed. Phoebe had to be talking about Woody. Woody was the only boy Kim had ever seen her with. Kim didn't know if she was strong enough to help Phoebe work out her feelings for Woody. But Phoebe's sad, green eyes stared at her, begging for help. Her freckles stood out across her nose, making her look very young and vulnerable.

"I'm not sure," began Kim. "I guess I'd have to question if this person really loved me. Have you told him how confused you feel?"

"Not really. I thought we understood each other without spelling things out all the time." She shook her head sadly. "I don't know if I should just forget the whole thing, or keep trying, or what."

"How much do you love him?" asked Kim, forgetting about her own problems momentarily in her desire to help Phoebe.

"More than anything in the world. He's so alive and wonderful. Even the dullest things seem interesting when he's around," Phoebe gushed, her eyes glowing. "I've never met anyone like him."

I know what you mean, Kim wanted to say. It was amazing how quickly Woody could energize the world and everyone around him. But he could also cause a lot of sadness, too, it seemed. Kim let her breath out slowly. The irony of it: She and Phoebe sitting here torn to pieces by the same guy.

"Kim? Do you ever wish you were ten years old again?" said Phoebe, her voice sounding small and lost.

"You mean back when our biggest problem was finding a plain old green crayon in those huge Crayola boxes?"

Phoebe laughed. "You got it."

"I don't know. I guess sometimes I do, but only when I'm really, super-depressed. It doesn't happen very often. Is that how you feel now?"

"Yeah . . . just watching my little brother get so excited about those stupid cartoons on TV. How simple everything is for him. At our age we seem to complicate our lives with all our questions like 'Who am I?' — 'What am I going to be when I grow up?' — 'What is love all about?' — 'Am I handling all this like I should?' — or, 'Am I blowing it because I'm so insecure?' Little things like that."

Kim laughed. "Whew! Now you're starting to sound like me."

Phoebe stared at her in disbelief. "You mean *you* feel like that, too?"

"At least every other day. It's funny. I'll be on a high, life really sailing along in fifth gear, then one morning I wake up and start questioning everything and what it means and how it affects me and how I'm going to deal with it. I guess those are the days I wish I were ten again."

Phoebe was still staring at Kim, open-mouthed. "Wow! But you seem so together and capable. . . ."

Kim laughed. "Beware the overly confident-looking types. Sometimes they aren't all they make themselves out to be."

"Gosh," sighed Phoebe. "Maybe there's hope for me yet."

"Of course there is," said Kim encouragingly. "You don't look like a loser to me, Phoebe."

Kim felt herself relax. The more they talked, the more she liked Phoebe. She was glad they'd finally gotten to know each other. If only this thing with Woody wasn't between them. She still didn't know what was going on, but it was time to get a few things straight. She took a deep breath.

"Phoebe, are you going to tell Woody how you feel?"

Phoebe looked at her in utter surprise. "Woody? What's Woody got to do with anything?"

Kim felt thoroughly confused. "But I thought. . . ."

"No . . . you didn't really . . ." stammered Phoebe and burst out laughing. "You didn't really think I was talking about Woody the whole time, did you? You think Woody drove me into Rosemont Park to sob to the dead roses?"

"Yes, but. . . ."

"Woody loves you so much," said Phoebe, still laughing. "He can't see beyond his own nose these days."

Kim felt the blood rush to her face.

Phoebe went on. "Haven't you noticed how he's been acting lately? I can barely recognize the guy, and I've known him for years."

"Well, his behavior has struck me as really weird, and to tell you the honest truth, I keep hoping the old Woody would come back," confessed Kim.

"Me, too," sighed Phoebe. "We went out together last night and he was so spaced out — spent the whole evening talking about you and how wonderful you are."

Kim stared at Phoebe, open-mouthed.

Phoebe giggled. "I can't believe you thought — anyway, it was my first night of freedom. I guess you've heard the terrible tale of Woody's car, and everyone else had a date, and I was feeling so down about Griffin, so I asked Woody to go to the movies with me."

"Who's Griffin?" asked Kim.

"The guy I've just been sobbing to you about." Phoebe paused, then looked Kim straight in the eye. "You're something, you know."

"Yeah, but don't tell me what," Kim giggled.

"No, be serious for a moment," broke in Phoebe. "I mean, here you thought I was talking about Woody — your boyfriend — the whole time, and still you were so nice to me — trying to help. You're wild. If it had been me, I probably would have scratched your eyes out."

Kim laughed. "I almost did, but do you know how pathetic you looked sitting in this rotting rose garden crying your heart out?"

Phoebe looked down. "Well, I want you to know I appreciate it. You may have just saved a life."

Kim put her arm around Phoebe. "Now tell me about Griffin. I hope this guy is worth all this."

The gleam that immediately lit up Phoebe's eyes convinced Kim he was.

"Oh, Kim, he's the most fabulous guy in the world . . . but the most confusing."

"Sounds like you *could* be talking about Woody," said Kim ruefully.

"I guess so; if he acts around you like he did around me last night, you've got one heavy scene to handle. I've never known him like this. That guy is in love with a capital L, I tell you. Really lost in space!"

"How long have you known Griffin?" asked Kim, trying to keep her mind off Woody.

"We only dated a few weeks before he went to New York to try out for some show. He wants to be an actor." Phoebe paused and looked searchingly around the rose garden. "But I knew we had something special. I still can't put my finger on it. But it was like the whole world suddenly looked different — the flowers more colorful, the sun yellower . . . do you know what I mean?"

Kim laughed. "I know exactly what you mean. That's how Woody affects me — when he's not lost on some one-way street in Nerdville."

"He's bound to come out of it," said Phoebe. "I've known him for six years, and he's never been this weird. You're just a whole new experience for him. He doesn't know how to deal with it."

Kim hadn't thought about this. Maybe she needed to be a little more patient with him. After all, she'd acted pretty weird when she and David started dating.

"Maybe you're a new experience for Griffin, too," said Kim. "Maybe he needs more time to work out all his feelings. After all, there's a lot going on for him right now. Making it as an actor in New York must be really tough."

"Yeah, you're right," replied Phoebe. "Maybe I've been selfish. Here I am, just in high school, but he's out in the real world trying to get his career going. It must be so hard."

"It seems to me if two people really have something, it'll survive all these tests," said Kim. "Like

Griffin being in New York and maybe just not having a lot of extra time for you right now."

"And Woody acting like a jerk," added Phoebe.

"Exactly. Maybe we both need a little more patience . . . and a lot of faith that it'll all work out if it's really meant to. Right?" Kim drew in a deep breath. "Whew, that all sounds wonderfully logical, doesn't it?"

Phoebe laughed. "But it's a good start. I needed that. I was headed into a major slump."

"You should stay involved in stuff at school," suggested Kim.

"Maybe I can do that again, now that I'm not grounded anymore," said Phoebe. "Any suggestions?"

"Well, the run-a-thon's Monday. I could sure use your help."

"Great," said Phoebe enthusiastically. "I'd love to. What time do you need me?"

"If you could get sixth period off and meet me at the track, that would be perfect." Kim was getting a little nervous about being the head honcho of this thing. Having Phoebe there would take a lot of the pressure off. Besides, they'd have a good time together. Kim felt that she and Phoebe could have a lot of good times together.

"You know what?" said Phoebe, giving Kim a crooked, self-conscious grin. "When Woody started getting interested in you, I got really jealous. Even though we were just friends, I'd always been his number-one girl. It was hard to give that up."

Kim laughed. "Don't think I wasn't jealous of you, too. I could tell you were really important to Woody, but I couldn't figure out just what the relationship was."

The girls burst out laughing and threw their arms around each other. Overhead the early birds of spring chattered away, and the sun beamed down warm and strong.

Chapter
11

"That's it for me," puffed Phoebe, after completing a mile on the track. "Scrubbing floors and painting shutters didn't do a thing for my cardiovascular system."

"Yeah, don't overdo it," said Kim, still jogging along. "I'm going for another mile, then I'll be over to help. Could you get the registration table set up?"

"Sure," said Phoebe, watching Kim's small, slender form move gracefully away from her. It was incredible how her opinion of Kim had changed in twenty-four hours, since they'd shared that time at Rosemont. She'd lost all her jealousy of Kim's drive and energy. Now they were working on a friendship that was real.

Kim's advice had worked wonders already. Phoebe had woken up that morning feeling really excited about life. Sure, the pain of Griffin was still there, but it didn't overwhelm her anymore. Kim was right; if she really believed she and Griffin had something special, then it would survive despite all the odds. Drowning in her own sorrow wasn't going to solve any of her problems. It was time to get on with things.

She unfolded the table and placed a couple of chairs behind it. On the front she taped up a sign announcing this was the registration area. It felt good to be doing something for her school again. She arranged the clipboards and pens. The cheerleaders were just coming out with their boxes of cookies, muffins, and cakes for the refreshment stand, followed by John Marquette and Ted Mason carrying a table for them. The coach jogged over from the gym and looked over the list of runners.

"This is one impressive list," he said. "Wish I could get this many kids to sign up for the track team."

Phoebe laughed. "Promise them a quarter a quarter mile and see what happens."

"I might have to do that. The core of our team graduated last year. I've never had so many losses." He concentrated on the list again. "By the way, was that you out there running with Barrie?"

"Yes," said Phoebe. "Why?"

"You've got a good stride. I think you'd make a decent quarter-miler. I suggest you try out for the team." He wandered off leaving Phoebe openmouthed. She'd never thought of being on a sports team. She'd never particularly cared if she were good at athletics or not. All she knew was that she was a lousy tennis player. But the coach thought she could run! Phoebe was flushed with pride. Maybe she ought to go out for the team. Why not?

"Pheeb." Chris came running toward her, looking tall, elegant, and graceful in her striped jogging shorts and matching sleeveless top. Phoebe wondered if her body would look more like that if she joined the track team. Definitely not tall. No hope of that, but she could slim down. Get rid of those extra five pounds that were always plaguing her.

"Oh, Pheeb, I feel terrible," said Chris. "I only realized this morning that you were officially free this Saturday. You must think I'm a real jerk for not calling and getting together."

"Naah . . . that's okay," said Phoebe.

"Well, I'm sorry. I guess I had just gotten so used to you not being able to do things, it didn't occur to me. Will you forgive me?"

Even though she did feel she should be a little mad at Chris for forgetting all about her, nothing could get Phoebe down right now. She felt great and gave her friend a big smile. "I'll only forgive you if you promise to take me on on the tennis court at least once a week. I'm determined to get good this year."

Chris laughed. "It's a deal. Let's start tomorrow afternoon."

"Great." Phoebe smiled to herself. Life was definitely getting back to normal. It seemed kind of dumb now to have let herself get so down.

"I better get out on that track before I find a dozen ways to convince myself this is a bad idea," said Chris, laughing.

"Okay. Let me check your name off. You're the first one, after Kim and me."

Kim was still breathing hard from the second mile she had run. The crowd was getting out sooner than she'd thought. The track area was full of people in all sorts of outfits — from color-coordinated jogging suits to gym shorts and T-shirts. She felt she should be there to greet them when they registered, but actually it looked as though Phoebe was handling everything just fine.

Kim watched Phoebe's shining face. She couldn't believe this was the same person she'd stumbled upon in the rose garden. Phoebe's whole body seemed to vibrate with a new kind of energy. Kim just hoped that things worked out for her and Griffin. Phoebe was obviously an extremely sensitive person. Kim picked up two glasses of water at the water station and wandered over to the registration table.

"How's it going?" she asked, handing Phoebe a glass.

"Thanks. Everything's moving right along." She stopped abruptly and stared past Kim. "Uh . . . oh. Here comes lover boy, looking pretty miserable."

Kim turned and saw Woody ambling toward them, all togged up to run. She wanted to run over and throw her arms around him. She'd missed him terribly. Especially after all Phoebe had told her. A huge smile spread over her face.

"Kim," he said plaintively. "I haven't seen you all day. Where've you been?"

Her smile faded. "I had to get things ready for this afternoon. You knew that."

"Yeah, but I figured you'd find time to stop by my locker — at least once."

"I'm sorry, Woody. I've just been running around like crazy." She held his hand. "But thank you for the beautiful flowers. They were wonderful."

"You liked them?" His face lit up.

"I loved them."

He kissed her lightly on the cheek. Her skin burned from his touch. Just a simple kiss, and her knees turned to jelly. Good thing she'd already run. Now she'd never make a hundred yards.

"Well, have you come out here to molest me?" she joked. "Or are you planning to actively participate in the First Annual Kennedy High Run-a-thon? With your love of jogging I expect nothing less than ten miles." Sitting at the table behind them, Phoebe grinned.

"I do love to run," insisted Woody seriously. "I can't wait to get on the track. Anything for the cause."

"Don't lie to me, Webster," said Kim in mock severity. "I know that deep within those sexy legs of yours cower the muscles of a true cyclist. But, I want you to know, I — and the Kennedy High girls' track team — appreciate your efforts."

"I'll show you 'my efforts,' " shot back Woody, and he ran out onto the track. His long legs ate up the ground.

Kim and Phoebe exchanged looks, then went back to work. One group of runners was waiting to get on the track; another was just coming off. There were more people than she'd expected in her wildest dream. It they could just clear eight hundred dollars, the girls' team could squeak by for another year. But eight hundred was big bucks.

"Whew, I'm going to get us a couple of cookies and some water," Kim said during a lull in the registration.

"Great," said Phoebe. "Things have slowed down a bit."

When Kim got to the water station she was surprised to see Woody flash by, still going around the track. He should have been finished five or ten minutes ago. She wandered over to one of the monitors.

"How's it going?" she asked casually.

"Terrific," said Mona, a freshman on the track team who had volunteered to help. "We've got some really determined people out there. That tall guy — Webster — looks like he's going to run all day. He's working on his third mile."

"Are you sure?" asked Kim. "That guy hates to run."

"I'm positive. He keeps reminding me how many laps he's done every time he passes."

Kim looked at Woody coming down the back stretch. His hair was soaked with sweat, but his legs were still moving rhythmically and powerfully. His hours of cycling were paying off for him — but he couldn't run forever. When he came by the water station, Kim handed him a cup of water. He took it without a smile.

"Hey, Woody, you've done great," yelled Kim. "Why not call it a day and come help me control the mobs?"

He didn't answer and actually picked up his pace. Kim shook her head. What was he trying to prove now? The old Woody would have shown up in some ridiculous costume and turned his two miles into a traveling road show.

Kim went over to the large chalk board and began writing up the big distance runners. Ted Mason had clocked in six miles and Brad had done five. Kim was surprised to see that Chris had managed five. Chris was athletic, but it took a lot of stamina to run five miles.

Kim swelled with pride. People were really coming out in big numbers and taking the run-a-thon seriously. At that moment, Kim felt she finally belonged to Kennedy High.

Kim snapped to when she saw Woody's red jogging shorts flash by. He was still running!

"Ted," called Kim, walking over to where he stood, his arm around Chris. They both looked tall, healthy, and beautiful. The perfect couple.

"Yeah," he answered. "You've really put on a great show here today, Kim. I'm impressed."

Kim blushed. "Thanks, Ted. Congrats on those six miles. You, too, Chris. Five miles is amazing."

"I really believe in what you're doing here, Kim. I wanted to help," said Chris, then smiling up at Ted, she continued. "Actually, I've been training a little, too. Super jock here had me out pounding the pavement every night for the past two weeks."

"You were getting flabby," he teased, rumpling her hair.

"Ha. You just wanted someone to keep you company while you ran off your baby fat."

147

"You're the best company in the world, even when you're nagging at me like my mommy," he said, as he pulled her in close to his side.

"Ted," broke in Kim. "I'm a little concerned about Woody."

"Oh, no. What's he up to now?" groaned Ted.

"I'm not sure," sighed Kim. "But I think he's out there trying to prove something to someone. He's been running for more than an hour now."

"My friend Woody has been running — I presume you mean his legs and not his mouth — for an hour!" exclaimed Ted. "That guy hates to run. What gives?"

"I don't know, but it seems kind of crazy to me."

"Crazy! It's completely wacko! He's going to hurt himself." Ted scanned the runners and finally picked out Woody. "Look at him. He's exhausted!"

"We've got to do something, Ted," begged Kim. "I mean, you've got to. I don't think he's too interested in listening to me right now."

Kim and Chris followed Ted to the track, keeping well in the background. Ted shouted something as Woody passed, but either Woody didn't hear or he pretended not to. His face was drained of color and his eyes were all glazed over.

"Ted, get him off the track the next time he comes around. He's going to hurt himself," called Kim. Ted nodded.

"He definitely does not look too good," said Chris in a worried voice.

Woody staggered around the far corner. Ted

stepped onto the track and grabbed his arm. Woody tried to pull away, but Ted wrapped both arms around him and lifted him onto the grass. Woody's legs gave out and he sank to the ground. Kim felt her heart beating wildly as she rushed over to him.

"Oh, Woody, you nut. Are you all right?" She brushed his damp curls out of his face. His eyes were dull and his skin clammy. "Better get the coach, Ted. And, Chris, could you bring me some wet towels from the locker room?"

Ted and Chris rushed off. In another minute the coach was kneeling down on the turf diagnosing Woody as dehydrated and exhausted. They placed the towels on his head and neck, and Kim carefully fed him sips of water. Slowly his color came back and his breathing returned to normal. When she was sure he was going to be all right, she threw her arms around him and squeezed him tightly.

"Woody, you scared the life out of me. What were you trying to do?" She was pale and shaky.

"You said you wanted me to go ten miles, so that's what I was going to do." He looked up at her with adoring eyes. "How far did I get?"

"You did nine, which was about seven too many."

"But think of all the money I made for you." His eyes shone.

"The object of this run-a-thon was for everyone to pitch in, not for one idiot to launch a crusade all on his own." Kim was angry now. He'd almost killed himself to prove something to her.

"Let me go run that extra mile. I want to make it ten," he begged. "Let me go." He tried to struggle to his feet.

"Woody Webster," Kim said, pushing him down, "I'm going to drive you home right now. You've got to rest. What you did out there was really off the wall. You could have screwed yourself up royally."

"Anything for you," he said quietly, holding her hand. Kim jerked her hand free.

"Come on. I've got my mom's car today. I'm taking you home. It's the red wagon by the gym door. I'll meet you there in a second. Now, go!"

Kim strode over to Phoebe. "Pheeb, can you handle things here? I've got to get Woody home."

"I heard. I'm sorry," replied Phoebe. "I hope you're able to knock some sense into him before he totally destroys himself."

"I'm beginning to wonder if it's worth it," said Kim in exasperation.

Phoebe put her arm on Kim's shoulders. "Remember what you told me about having faith. Please have faith in Woody. He's worth it, I promise."

Kim could only manage a weak smile, but she did feel a little stronger.

"Don't worry. I can take over from here. Things are moving pretty smoothly," said Phoebe. "You just look after Woody."

Kim didn't know how to approach him as they drove along silently. But she knew she had to say something, even if it threatened their relationship.

"Woody," she finally said in a controlled, even voice.

"Yes," he replied eagerly.

"Things aren't going very well with us, are they?"

"What do you mean? Everything's perfect. I think you're wonderful. Absolutely the best."

"Well, I don't think you're so wonderful sometimes. I don't know why you're doing it, but it's like you're losing yourself somehow. You used to be so much fun and now I don't even know who you are anymore. What's happening?"

"Oh, Kim," said Woody in a wounded voice. "I'm just trying to please you. You mean everything to me."

Something broke in Kim, she'd had enough of this soppy routine. "I don't want to be pleased," she said, trying to keep her voice under control. "I don't want you groveling at my feet, sending me flowers, saying my cookies are good when I know they're rotten. I don't want any of that. I want the old Woody back; that wonderful person who made me laugh. You remember. The one who did the corniest imitations of Gene Kelly I've ever seen." Kim sighed deeply. "I can't take it anymore, Woody. I'm obviously destroying you, and you're destroying me. Something is terribly wrong. It would have been better if we'd just stayed friends."

"What are you saying, Kim?" asked Woody, hurt written all over his face. "I've gone out of my way to do everything for you. I've tried to be nice. What do you want? Some jerk like John Marquette? He's a friendly character, all right.

151

His idea of being nice to a girl is ordering her to pick him up, then demanding favors and getting irked when she doesn't bow and scrape. Is that what you want?"

Kim shook her head slowly. "Oh, Woody, I just want you — Woody Webster. The one I met at Ted Mason's party. I haven't seen him for so long. If you see him, tell him I miss him very, very much." Kim pulled up to the curb in front of Woody's house.

"Well, maybe you won't ever see him around," said Woody, and Kim could hear the hurt in his voice. It broke her heart. How had things gotten to this point so quickly?

"Maybe it would be a good idea if we just cool it for a while," said Kim, trying to be calm and rational. "Give each other some breathing space, and see what happens. Maybe we can start all over."

"Fine with me," shouted Woody, slamming the car door. "Absolutely perfect with me."

Kim watched him stomp off, her heart slowly tearing into a million pieces.

Chapter **12**

Kim wished the sun weren't so warm and cheerful. She would have preferred a gray day; the kind she could wrap around her sadness and find comfort in. Somehow the beauty of this sunny day only emphasized how desolate she felt. The image of Woody angrily stomping away from her had plagued her all night, and was just as vivid in the light of day. She'd tried to approach him several times at school, to at least try to talk things out, but each time he'd looked right through her and passed down the hall without a word. Kim didn't know whether to burst into tears or scream at the top of her lungs. She just knew she hurt. But there was one thing she knew: Somehow she had to get Woody to talk. Everything was getting blown way out of proportion, and this hostile silence wasn't helping at all.

Kim cycled slowly down Main Street. She didn't feel like collecting her pledges, but it had to be done. She'd promised the track team a report by Wednesday morning. They were desperate to know the outcome; their season's success or failure hung on it. Right now she didn't even care what the result was. Nothing seemed to matter. She wanted to go home and sleep for a week or two, then wake up and have everything be back to normal. That was a coward's attitude, she knew, but she didn't care. All her energy had been drained.

A wave of nostalgia hit her when she locked her bike to the same pole she and Woody had used when they'd signed up pledges together that wonderful, magical, unbelievable day. All that intensity, all that emotion down the tubes. That was the saddest part. She and Woody were perfect together, but they weren't together.

Kim collected at the beauty salon and several other places and was heading into the butcher's, when Woody came out of the news store and started into the same door. They looked at each other, and time was suspended. Her feelings for Woody, her confusion over what was going on, blocked out everything else. Maybe he would apologize and they could begin again, right there, this afternoon. They could share a milkshake on Rose Hill and watch the sun set with their arms wrapped around each other. Kim swallowed hard. More than anything she wanted things to be back to normal with Woody. She'd even settle for their old friendship. Anything except this cold war.

"Hi," she said, unsure if even that was the right thing to say. Then she added, "What's a nice guy like you doing in a place like this?" She glanced at the window with all the hams and sausages. Woody's sour expression didn't change at all.

"Collecting pledges, obviously," he said coldly. "Isn't that what you ordered us all to do?"

Kim's heart sank. No chance of a reconciliation here. "How are you feeling?" she asked. "You really ran your buns off yesterday. No permanent damage, I hope."

"I'm afraid it'll take more than a few lousy miles to get Woody Webster down," he said sarcastically. "Although I must admit, I don't think the cause was worth all that effort on my part."

"Hey, kids, come on in," said Mr. Moser, swinging open the door. "Guess you've come to hit me up for my pledge, huh? How'd you do?"

Kim forced a smile. After all, these people were helping the school out. "Great. At least I think so. We've just started collecting."

"How many miles did you make?" asked the butcher, going back to his work. Steaks fell thick and fast under his cleaver. Kim watched in fascination, wishing she had something to pound on like that to get rid of her frustrations.

"I managed two," said Kim modestly, "but Woody went nine. Almost ten."

The butcher looked up with surprise. "Wow. You kids are going to put me in the poor house, but I'm proud of you. Let's see, that means I owe you forty-eight dollars." He opened his cash register and handed them the money. "Yep, I'm very proud of you. I hope this gets those girls to their meets."

"Thank you so much, Mr. Moser," said Kim,

stashing the money in the roomy pockets of her paratrooper pants. "We really appreciate it."

"Well . . . we're all part of this community. Might as well try to help each other out if we can." He paused, cleaver in midair. "Oh, yes. Tell your mother that that lamb has come in. Looks mighty good, too." He smiled at Kim and gave Woody a wink. "They had their papers all in order. Just like I said."

"Are you just tossing that money in your pocket?" asked Woody when they got outside.

"Yes," said Kim. "These are big pockets. They'll hold it fine."

"I think that's really dumb. Why don't you carry it in a bag like this?" he said, holding up a paper bag. "This is what I'm using."

"Now that's super dumb, if you don't mind my saying so. You could easily throw that away thinking it was just a trash bag."

"Do you think I'd be stupid enough to throw away a wad of money?" argued Woody.

"Anyone might throw it away. It's just an old bag. At least I know there's no chance of me throwing my pants away." Kim knew this argument was foolish, but she couldn't help herself. Woody was out of control. Somehow she had to bring him back to reality. If it meant bringing herself down to his level, then down she'd go.

"It could fall out. There's no zipper or button to keep it in," he said, beginning to walk faster and faster. Kim was almost jogging to keep up.

"Do you think the army'd design trousers so things fell out?" she demanded angrily. He really was unreasonable. "Can't you just see a soldier in the middle of a battle running around in the trenches with stuff falling out of his pockets? Ha!"

"They keep their stuff in rucksacks, not in their pockets," retorted Woody. "And, do you want to know why they keep it in their rucksacks?"

"I can't wait to hear this," snapped Kim.

"So it doesn't fall out of their pockets."

"And do you know why they don't carry their stuff around in paper bags?" asked Kim heatedly. "Well, I'll tell you. Because brown paper bags get thrown away. Most people think of them as trash bags. That's why."

"You know, you're really boring me," said Woody. "If you're so great, why don't you just collect the stuff yourself?" He handed his bag to Kim and walked off before she could reply. Kim watched him go, her whole body shaking with anger.

"Where's that nice young man you had with you last time?" asked Mrs. Stenson when Kim got to the farmers' market.

She smiled at Mrs. Stenson despite her anger and explained that Woody was so exhausted after doing almost ten miles that she was collecting for him.

"Ten miles! Goodness gracious!" She called to the back of the store. "Alf. Come on out here." Mr. Stenson shuffled to the front, loaded down by a box of lettuce.

"Alf, remember that nice boy who taught you

how to juggle? He ran ten miles in that thing up at the school. Ten miles! Can you believe it?"

"Sure I can. If he taught me to juggle in five minutes, I imagine he can do just about anything. Had that air about him."

Kim couldn't deny she was swelling with pride. They were talking about Woody. Her Woody. And secretly, she agreed with every word they said.

"I was hoping to show him how good I've gotten," said Mr. Stenson. "I'm up to four oranges now." He plucked four fat oranges from a box and began to juggle. Around and around they went. Mr. Stenson's face was beaming.

"That's wonderful," exclaimed Kim when he finally reboxed them. "That's really great, Mr. Stenson. I'll tell Woody. I know he'll be impressed."

"Here, take him this sack of apples," said Mr. Stenson. "They're good for what ails you."

I wish it were that simple, thought Kim, smiling and accepting the bag. Mr. and Mrs. Stenson paid their pledge money and promised to try to make it to a track meet. Kim walked away with that warm feeling the Stensons always left with her.

Kim finished her collecting and headed home. She knew by the weight of the bag that things had gone well, but when she counted it later and discovered she'd collected two hundred twenty-three dollars and fifty cents, she couldn't believe it. She still wished Woody hadn't almost destroyed himself, but she had to admit his efforts had paid off. The others were turning their money in after lunch tomorrow, by the end of the day she'd know the grand total.

"Kim, dear, I need those boxes at the side, not in the back," called out Kim's mother. "It's important that they get into the freezer immediately."

Kim quickly rearranged the boxes. Her mind just wouldn't snap into gear this morning. She'd had to wake up very early to help her mother. And she'd been awake half the night trying to figure Woody out, trying to decide what to do about their relationship. Half the time, she'd convinced herself they really weren't made for each other and should call it quits.

The rest of the time she kept seeing the sun filtering through the pine trees at Rosemont, spotlighting the mushrooms and toadstools, and remembering the feel of Woody's body next to hers. It had been so right. But if they were so perfect together, why did it seem that they were slowly destroying each other? Her head was spinning.

"Dear, I hate to ask you," said Mrs. Barrie, "but would you come with me to The Cliff House? I want to get this stuff in the freezer as soon as possible, and something tells me I won't be able to count on Mrs. Fitch to lend a hand. I'll drop you at school."

Her mother was delivering the boxed meals to Mrs. Fitch that day, and for the first time since they had started Earthly Delights, Kim could tell her mother was nervous. It had been a big order and she wasn't sure how some of the food would weather the trip from their freezer to Mrs. Fitch's.

159

Kim smiled. "Of course, Mom. I have study hall first period, anyway. I'm sure Mrs. Martin will understand." She threw her books, lunch bag, and the bag full of money into the car.

They'd soon left the city limits behind and were winding through the beautiful Maryland countryside. Kim settled back to watch the early morning world, trying desperately not to think about Woody.

"Oh, Mrs. Barrie, I'm so glad you've come," said Mrs. Fitch as she let them in the kitchen door. "I'm going to put those meals right to work. The local chapter of the DAR — I'm the president, you know — is meeting here for lunch. What do you recommend I serve?"

"You have lamb, veal, or chicken meals," replied Kim's mother professionally. "I would suggest the lamb for a midday meal. It's light, but savory — fresh from New Zealand."

Even hearing her mother say "New Zealand" hurt. Kim recalled Woody's hilarious routine with Mr. Moser about the spring lambs and their visa problems. They'd had such fun that day. Kim sighed.

"Oh, that does sound good," babbled Mrs. Fitch.

"Then we'll leave out the lamb and put the others in the freezer," concluded Mrs. Barrie. "If you could just show us where the freezer is, we'll get these bags in quickly. I don't want anything to thaw."

Mrs. Fitch bustled around the Barries while they hauled the sacks down to the basement

160

freezer. She never offered to help, just kept up a steady stream of chatter that began to annoy Kim. She was glad to finally leave.

"Good-bye, dear," said her mother as Kim grabbed all her stuff and slid out of the car in front of the Kennedy entrance.

"Good-bye, Mom," said Kim. "See you to-night."

"Thanks for your help. I really needed you today."

Chapter
13

"Happy lunch hour, everyone. This is your wounded hero, Peter Lacey, of WKND. I don't know about the rest of you, but my muscles are still in revolt over Monday's misuse. But it was all for a good cause. Right? Of course it was 'cause we've got one class-act girls' track team that deserves our support. Let's just hope that next year the school board can find it in their hearts and wallets to come up with the extra bucks, so the rest of us don't have to self-destruct on the track." He laughed. "Now listen up. Pledge money, as you all know, is due in by two o'clock this afternoon. Coach Harvey will be in the gym to collect. Someone keep an eye on him, though. We all know how badly he wants a vacation in the Bahamas this year."

Kim rolled her eyes at Phoebe, and they both burst out laughing. They'd just finished lunch and were heading off to their lockers to get their pledge money.

Kim had been on pins and needles all morning, anxious to get her money turned in and to add up the total. She hoped it would be impressive. All the kids had really worked hard to make the run-a-thon happen. She didn't want anyone to be disappointed.

Kim flew to her locker, almost crashing into Woody as she tore around the corner at the top of the stairs.

"Excuse me," mumbled Kim, sliding by him.

"Yeah," he said, sauntering over to his own locker.

Kim worked the combination on the door, watching Woody all the time out of the corner of her eye. He was trying to be cool, acting like she didn't exist; but book after book fell loudly on the floor as he fumbled around, searching for the one he wanted. Kim knew he was upset. I hope he had a sleepless night, too, she said to herself. Why should I be the only one to suffer?

Another book crashed to the floor, jangling Kim's nerves. I've got to get out of here, she thought, and reached for the money bag. Her hand grabbed air. She threw the door open wide. It wasn't there! She looked in the bottom of her locker, rummaging through books and gym clothes, but nothing. Maybe she'd put it on top. She hardly ever put anything on the top shelf because she was too short to be able to see to the back.

Standing on tiptoe, she ran her hand back and forth across the shelf. Again . . . nothing. Her heart was beginning to pound in fear. There was two hundred dollars in that bag — more than two hundred! How could she ever replace it if she'd lost it? She tried to think rationally, but her mind was so befuddled she couldn't even remember if she'd left home with one bag or two.

Her tummy did a couple of slow, laborious flops. How was she going to explain the disappearance to the coach and to the rest of the gang?

"Oh, nooooo," groaned Kim, sinking down on her heels to have one more look at the bottom of her locker. But she already knew that she wouldn't find anything.

"What's wrong?" asked Woody, trying to sound casual, yet with an unmistakable note of concern in his voice. He slammed his locker and came over.

"I can't find the money," said Kim in despair. "It's gone."

"What money?" began Woody. Then it hit him. "You don't mean the pledge money?" He was stuttering in disbelief. "What happened?"

"That's just it. I don't know," said Kim, her eyes brimming with tears. "I honestly don't know. I put it in here this morning — at least I thought I did — and now it's gone."

"Let me look," he said, gently moving her aside. He rummaged through the locker, top and bottom, pulling everything out onto the floor. Nothing.

For a moment he and Kim sat side by side on the floor staring forlornly at the piles of stuff.

"How much was in it?" asked Woody finally.

"Two hundred twenty-three dollars and fifty cents," said Kim almost inaudibly.

"Two hundred twenty-three-fifty!" exclaimed Woody, leaping to his feet. "You've lost two hundred twenty-three-fifty? Half of that's my money, too."

"Well maybe you should have collected it yourself," retorted Kim, staring hotly up at him. "Then at least you wouldn't be wasting your energy yelling at me now."

"Wait a minute, Kim," he said, putting his hands on her shoulders to calm her down. "Getting mad at each other isn't going to solve this problem. We've got to be calm — we've got to *think* — and think fast! That money is due in today."

"I know. I know," moaned Kim. She wracked her brain silently for a second, then exclaimed, "Wait a minute! Mother and I delivered a whole bunch of frozen food to Mrs. Fitch's this morning. And it was all packed in brown paper bags. Just like the one the money was in." She looked at Woody expectantly.

"No," he said, shaking his head. "It can't be true. Are you trying to tell me the money is on ice — safely packed away in Senator Fitch's freezer? That has got to be the dumbest thing I ever heard."

"It wouldn't have happened if you hadn't had the great idea of putting the money in a brown paper bag. I told you something might happen, but you wouldn't listen. Woody Webster knows best. Ha!" Kim was shaking with rage.

"Hold on a second. You can't blame this one on me," shouted Woody. "If I had known you were such a pea-brain I would have suggested you hire an armored car to follow you around."

"Don't you call me a pea-brain, Webster."

"What would you suggest I call you after this little stunt? I find *brilliant* kind of inappropriate, don't you?"

"Good heavens," cooed Laurie, wandering up. "If you two are going to start throwing things. . . . May I salvage the math book at least? Mine's in such bad shape."

"Look, Laurie, Woody and I were just having a little discussion. Do you mind?" said Kim.

"If that's your idea of a 'little discussion,' I'd sure hate to be around when you get in an argument." She turned to Woody. "Woody Webster, I'm surprised at you. I didn't think you'd stoop so low to be caught screaming in the halls."

"I wasn't screaming," said Woody defensively. "But you want to know the brilliant thing Kim did?"

"I don't think Laurie's the least big interested, Woody," growled Kim.

"I'm all ears," said Laurie, her eyes gleaming.

"She accidentally packed away two hundred dollars of run-a-thon pledge money in Senator Fitch's freezer."

Laurie laughed, looking puzzled.

"We don't know for sure that's where it is," said Kim hotly.

"Well, I don't know if you'd be interested in a little inside info," said Laurie conspiratorially, moving closer to them and glancing up and down

166

the hall. "But Brenda Austin was in your locker a couple of days ago. Of course, I'm not suggesting anything, but I definitely saw her open the lock and rummage around in there."

"Sorry, Laurie, but for once I think you're wrong," said Kim, starting to reload her locker. "I gave Brenda my combination so she could store her present for Brad in here."

"Well, if she had the combination, who knows how many times she's been in there," retorted Laurie after a moment's hesitation. "We all know about Brenda, don't we, Woody?" Without another word, she sauntered off down the hall.

"That girl gives me the creeps," Kim said with exasperation. "What are we 'all' supposed to know about Brenda?"

Woody shuffled his feet and looked around uneasily.

"Well . . . ?" asked Kim.

"Uh . . . it happened a long time ago," said Woody, looking more uncomfortable.

"What happened? Come on, out with it."

"When Brenda first came to Rose Hill, things didn't seem to work out real well — living with Chris and her dad, and all."

"I know that, but I don't see what it has to do with the missing money."

"Well, Brenda ran away and got in with a bad crowd. I think Laurie was just saying that Brenda's the only one she could think of who might possibly do something like take the money from your locker. Especially if she had the combination."

"Oh, Woody, I can't believe Brenda would do

that. She's one of the nicest girls at this school. I mean, at least as far as I'm concerned, she is. No, I just don't believe it — Brenda would never take advantage of our friendship like that."

"I hope you're right," said Woody quietly.

Chapter
14

Kim looked up and down the street. A few cars whizzed by. There was a man walking an unbelievably small dog — it looked more like a big, brown rat on a leash. A man and a woman jogged by in matching blue shorts, but no Woody. Kim's heart pounded, and her hands were sweaty with fear. He had to show. He just had to. He'd promised to help her find the money. Fortunately she'd been able to talk the principal into delaying his announcement of the run-a-thon grand total for twenty-four hours. She had twenty-four hours to come up with the money. The coach told her he'd already collected more than seven hundred dollars from the other kids. The money from her and Woody would boost the amount to over nine hundred dollars — more than enough to keep the girls' team afloat for another year. But only if Kim and Woody found the money.

Woody just couldn't let her down. She glanced

at her watch. Two minutes to three. Well, he wasn't even officially late yet. Taking a deep breath, she continued her search up and down the street. Finally she spotted a lone figure cycling toward her. She knew it was Woody, even from this distance. Her body told her; her tummy fluttered anxiously, and her knees went weak. As he got closer she could see the mischievous gleam in his eyes and the wind whipping his curls. The old Woody. For a second Kim almost forgot her troubles — the money, Woody's weird mood — and smiled.

"Hi," he said cheerily, pulling to a halt beside her. "Want to know what I've been thinking?"

"As long as it's legal and safe, sure," she quipped.

"Legal, yes. Safe . . . sort of," he said, his grin widening. "Actually, it's probably not even legal."

"Uh, oh," said Kim, rolling her eyes. "Let's hear it. If this will help us get the money back, I'm even willing to consider illegal and dangerous. What bank do you want to bust?"

"Why, Madame, you underestimate me," replied Woody with mock indignation. "Anyone can rob a bank. I'm talking about the refined art of breaking and entering."

Kim started to laugh, then stopped abruptly. He was serious.

"I think we ought to assume for the moment that the money is, indeed, at the Fitch estate. I'm not even going to let myself think that Brenda was involved until we've checked all the other possibilities," he said.

"Right. But we can't exactly walk up, ring the

front door bell, and ask permission to rummage through Mrs. Fitch's freezer. Knowing that lady, she'd smoke us for hams and serve us up at her next luncheon — not to mention what it would do to Earthly Delights' fragile status. Right now Mrs. Fitch is mother's most important account. Just from the DAR lunch yesterday, my mother got three new customers. I can't jeopardize that."

"She's that bad, huh?" asked Woody skeptically.

"Worse."

"Good."

"Good?" Kim stared at Woody wide-eyed. "The woman's an absolute tyrant. What's good about that?" All at once it hit her. She and Woody were back to normal. At least back to the way their old friendship used to be: They were arguing, but they weren't trying to hurt each other anymore. They were planning an adventure together.

"It's good, because now we get to put my brilliant plan into action," said Woody.

"Okay, let's hear it," said Kim.

"We agree we can't approach this woman head on, right?"

"Right."

"So I suggest I divert her while you sneak down in the basement and check out the freezer."

"Woody! That's nuts. What would you possibly do to divert her? Steal the chandelier in the dining room? Pose as a Fuller Brush man? — no, bag that — I don't think she's the type who would buy a Fuller Brush." Kim shook her head in mock dismay. "Wait a minute — I've got it. How about posing as an encyclopedia salesman? I'm sure she must need a new set of encyclopedias for the library. A senator has to do his research, after all." Kim shook her head again, this time in real frustration. "No, Woody, for once I don't think your plan will work."

"Now wait a minute. Hear me out, at least," he said in exasperation. "You know, that's one of your biggest problems . . . you never listen to other people. You're always charging ahead with your own ideas like Custer at his last stand, and you *know* what happened to him." He ran his finger across his throat to emphasize the point.

"I thought we were trying to recover the money, not tote up my faults," said Kim sarcastically, but part of her knew that Woody was right.

"We are, we are," said Woody. "Sorry."

"No, I'm sorry. Go ahead."

"Okay. Well, I thought that I could pose as head of the Student Better Government Committee and keep Mrs. Fitch busy with a lot of questions about the senator and his policies, while you sneak down to the basement and check things out. What do you think?"

"I think it's completely crazy, but I don't see what other choice we have," said Kim. "We've got to find that money, and I'll do anything to prove that Laurie's wrong about Brenda."

"Then, let's go," said Woody excitedly, as he took off on his bike.

They raced along. The streets of the town turned into country lanes, and in no time they found themselves at the bottom of the long drive to The Cliff House.

"You know what, Webster?" asked Kim.

"What — you've decided I'm a pretty brilliant planner?" He laughed.

"We haven't pulled it off yet, so I'm not willing to commit myself," retorted Kim good-naturedly. "But I do think that, to you, this is one big stage production. You've got the script down, the sequence of action, your cues, mine. . . ."

Woody gave her a big grin. "I can't deny it. You're absolutely right. It's been a long time since my last production. I need a fix."

Kim giggled. "Well, let's just hope the curtain doesn't come down on us prematurely."

"I know exactly what you mean." He laughed. "Okay. Now, let's go. Leave your bike here, in the ditch. When you've frisked the freezer, come straight back here. I'll try to keep Mrs. Fitch talking for at least that long. I'll meet you here. Okay?"

"Hey, who am I to question? You're the stage manager. I'm just a lowly actor."

"If you play your part well, you'll be amply rewarded. Just bear that in mind." He winked at her, then headed up the drive. Kim's tummy did a backflip. She raced after him.

At a fork in the driveway, Woody wheeled his bike up to the front entrance while Kim headed back to the kitchen door. She stayed hidden in a big boxwood bush by the entrance until she heard Mrs. Fitch answer the front door. Then, peeping in the window to be sure no one was in sight, she quietly and slowly tried the kitchen door. It was open. She slipped through. Once inside, she stood still, listening, her heart pounding double time. For a second she didn't think Woody had gotten inside. She heard voices and recognized Mrs. Fitch's semihysterical tones. But the other voice, although it was deep and rich like Woody's, had a distinct Southern accent.

"Well, like I said, Miz Fitch," he drawled. "I'm president of the Student Better Government Committee over at Kennedy High. I'm sure you know the reelection in many states is now an issue that calls for national party effort. We in the B.G.C. are committed to that effort. High school students can make a significant difference to the Senator's reelection prospects."

"You're absolutely right, of course," chirped Mrs. Fitch. "I'll be sure to remind the Senator of that. He just loves all you young folks, so I'm sure he'll be most willing to cooperate with all your efforts on his behalf."

Kim had to cover her mouth to keep from laughing out loud. Woody was giving the performance of his life. Kim had never heard Mrs. Fitch sound so polite and accommodating. She had to mentally kick herself to get on with her mission; she'd have loved to just stand there and admire Woody's acting. Instead, she crept stealthily over to the basement door and started down the steps.

The basement was dank and smelled of centuries of canned goods, dried gourds, and leaky pipes. She descended the steps slowly, not wanting to turn on the light. The small fifteen-watt bulb in the freezer would give her plenty to see by. She felt her way along the wall, cringing when she touched a cobweb or damp spot — the dangers inherent in her mission washing over her anew. What in the world would she say if she were caught? Why did she let Woody talk her into this madness? Just because he had to satisfy his craving to put on a play, she'd gotten sucked into this insanity.

Finally she found the freezer and was about to lift the lid when the basement door suddenly swung open. Kim dropped behind the freezer and held her breath. This was it! Mrs. Fitch had seen through Woody, called her servants, and tortured him into telling her where his accomplices were. Kim knew her imagination was running wild, but the footsteps had descended the stairs and were making their way steadily toward the exact spot where she was hidden.

"Hmmmm. Let me see . . ." mumbled a voice. Kim couldn't see who it was, but it sounded like Mrs. Fitch's maid. The freezer lid opened, and a beam of light splashed on the floor just inches away. All Kim's muscles were taut and aching. Her lungs begged for air.

Whoever it was fumbled around in the freezer for a few more seconds, then shuffled back up the stairs. Finally, when it was all quiet again, Kim let her breath out in a painful rush. She jumped to her feet and opened the freezer. It was filled with brown bags. Kim stared in dismay. There were so many of them. There was nothing to do but start going through them, one by one. She lifted each bag out, unfolded the top, and peeked inside. One bag after another was filled with Earthly Delights dinners, all neatly packaged and labeled. Kim searched on; becoming more and more frantic. Maybe Laurie was right after all.

Could Brenda have taken the money? No! It had to be here, it just had to. Brenda just was not that kind of person. Kim continued her search.

Tears stung her eyes. She'd been through almost every bag and still no money. As each minute passed, she was surer and surer she was going to get caught. Not even Woody could keep Mrs. Fitch talking as long as she'd been in that basement. Finally, she noticed a bag over in the corner that wasn't the same neat, rectangular shape as the others. Grabbing it, she almost ripped off the top. It was there! The money! Quickly she rearranged the bags in the freezer and scurried upstairs, the bag clasped tightly under her arm.

She listened carefully at the kitchen door, then, convinced there was no one there, she pushed it gently open. It squeaked and groaned in protest. Kim slipped through the narrow opening and out the back door just as someone entered the kitchen from the dining room. She didn't look back but, keeping close to the boxwood hedge, raced down the driveway. Woody rushed up to meet her.

"Geez, where have you been? I was getting ready to send in the Feds," he said, throwing an arm around her shoulders. Kim leaned into him, sighing with relief.

"I've got it," she said weakly. "Here." She thrust the bag at him and retrieved her bike from the weeds. "Let's get out of this horrible place."

Kim almost didn't have the strength to pedal, but pedal she did. She wanted to put about three million miles between herself and Mrs. Fitch. Maybe four million.

By the time they hit the familiar streets of Rose Hill Kim's heart had begun to beat normally again. She followed Woody into the park, where they immediately dropped their bikes on the grass and flopped down. Woody burst out laughing.

"We did it, Kim! We did it!" He rolled over on his side and looked at her face. "We just pulled off the perfect heist." He rumpled her hair.

"Jesse James would have been proud of us." She laughed, weak with relief. She was definitely not gangster material, the afternoon had proven that. But now that it was over, she had to admit it actually was fun.

"Jesse James, Ma Barker, the whole crew would have been proud. You should have seen me sweet-talking Mrs. Fitch. She was eating out of the palm of my hand," said Woody, howling up at the clouds.

"Well, while you were having a social hour with the Senator's wife, yours truly, here, was risking her life in the dank, dark basement. I almost got caught."

"No! What happened?!" Woody turned to her again.

Kim told him the whole story: about the maid coming in and her hiding behind the freezer, then not being able to find the money until the very end.

"Yeah, I was sure beginning to wonder what had happened to you. But I figured if you'd taken the money and run, you'd at least send me a postcard. I need a Brazilian stamp for my collection anyway."

Kim laughed and punched him in the arm. "You nut. We could have gotten ourselves into a lot of trouble."

"But it was worth it. Here, look at all this stuff Mrs. Fitch gave me," said Woody, emptying his backpack on the grass.

Kim balanced her glasses on her nose and looked over the stacks of posters, pamphlets, and flyers of Senator Fitch.

"I still think you look sexy in those specs," teased Woody.

Kim felt color leap to her cheeks. "I don't know why I let you talk me into all this," she said, searching for something to say.

"Because I'm so old and wise," said Woody with a grin. "Besides, you need me."

Kim looked at him seriously for a second. I did need him, she thought to herself.

"Let's not forget who got us in this mess in the first place," said Kim with a sly smile.

"Surely you're not suggesting that . . . I . . . no, you couldn't be," he said in mock horror.

"Oh yes I could. Putting the money in that paper bag was dumb. D-U-M-B . . . dumb," said Kim.

"Yeah," conceded Woody. "I guess you're right." He turned to her with a mischievous grin. "I get us into trouble. I get us out of trouble. The main thing is we have the money, and we were right about Brenda."

"Thank goodness. You know, for just a moment when I was going wacko down there looking into all those brown bags, I found myself wondering if maybe she had taken it. Isn't it funny how the human mind works sometimes? We can get sucked into believing such stupid things." Kim stared down at the ground, lost in thought. She'd almost been willing to call Brenda a thief.

"Yeah. Look at us," said Woody, pulling her chin up so she was looking him directly in the eye. "We almost ruined a perfectly good friendship over a brown paper bag."

"Your brown paper bag," joked Kim, throwing another punch at him. In a flash his hand grabbed hers and pushed her flat on her back. Kim squealed and tried to free herself, kicking playfully at his feet, but Woody held her firmly. They rolled over and over in the grass, laughing and trying to pin each other down.

Woody's mouth found hers. For a second Kim thought about protesting, but his touch was so gentle and coaxing. Kim sighed and gave herself up to the wonderful sensation that she thought she'd only dreamed. Woody Webster had completely disoriented her again, but this time she knew it was okay. Her old Woody was back. Her crazy clown. Her warm, wonderful friend.

Kim wrapped her arms more tightly around him and reveled in the warmth of his embrace. She snuggled her face into his neck and nipped him playfully.

"Ouch," Woody cried, leaping back. His eyes twinkled. "If you're that hungry, I'll get you a milkshake. All you had to do was ask."

Kim gave him a mischievous look. "A milkshake wouldn't do it right now, and I don't care how many strawberries they put in it."

Woody entwined his fingers in her hair and

gently pulled her face to his. Kim felt she could stare into his eyes forever. The air around crackled with its own invisible sparks, and her body felt like it was floating two feet above the ground.

"Kim," said Woody eventually, wrapping her in close to his chest. "I want to apologize."

"Hmmmmmm," sighed Kim. His heart pounded away under her ear.

"No, I mean it. I'm serious. I've been acting like a complete jerk for the past week. I'm sorry."

"Kiss me one more time, and all is forgiven," said Kim, turning her cheek to him.

Woody pulled her in tightly and sealed her mouth with his. Kim didn't care about tomorrow. She didn't care about yesterday. This moment was all that mattered — this moment lost in the magic of Woody Webster. Her Woody.

"I love you, Kim," whispered Woody, covering her neck with soft kisses. "I love you so much."

Kim pulled back and looked him straight in the eye. "I love you, too," she said softly.

"Good!" he said flippantly. "Now that we've agreed on the important stuff, let's get down to basics."

In a flash Kim found herself pulled across his body in a theatrical pose. Then he kissed her with a loud smack.

"You nut," said Kim, laughing as she struggled to a sitting position. Woody smiled tenderly down at her and pulled her back to his chest, very gently this time.

"You know," he said. "Loving someone is a whole new thing for me." He smoothed her hair gently back from her forehead. "And I'm afraid

I'm making all my mistakes on you. I guess I've been trying to act like the script says someone in love is supposed to. Maybe I've been seeing too many B movies lately." He hesitated, then looked at her sheepishly. "I've been a real jerk, haven't I?"

"As a matter of fact . . . yes," agreed Kim, kissing his chest lightly.

"Then why did you put up with me?" Woody asked.

Kim squeezed him hard. "Because I believed in you, Woody. I figured you had to come back sometime . . . and I was right, huh?!" Kim laughed and hung her head. "Anyway, you're not the only one who's been acting like a jerk. I've been working so long on my independence act, I'd really talked myself into thinking I didn't need anyone else. I guess the lesson I learned in the past week is that I need you very, very much." She looked earnestly up into Woody's face. "Loving someone — I mean really loving him — seems to mean giving up part of yourself. I've never done that before. It scares me."

"Aw, come on — don't be scared," whispered Woody, kissing the top of her head. "It's okay to need me. I want you to need me. That's what was driving me nuts last week, making me act so crazy. I didn't want to be just the guy in your life who kept you supplied with great jokes. I wanted us to be a team, to need each other." He held her at arm's length and stared deeply into her eyes. "Don't kid yourself. I need you, too." He paused, then gave her a wide grin. "Who else would be crazy enough to break into Senator

181

Fitch's house with me?" He threw back his head and laughed. "I love you, Kimberlation."

"And I love you, Woody. So, so much," she said and squeezed him until she thought her arms would break.

Chapter
15

Phoebe wandered slowly down the street, trying to figure out what she was feeling. *Fragile* was the best word she could come up with. Very fragile. Not depressed, and certainly not as happy as this warm spring evening warranted. Just fragile. Like she didn't know if she wanted to burst into tears, or run full tilt through the park. Maybe she shouldn't have let Sasha talk her into calling Griffin one more time. They'd been minding Sasha's parents' store all afternoon so Sasha had had a long time to work on her.

"Ah come on, Pheeb," said Sasha. "Give him one more chance. Be tough. Ask him right out if he wants to call the relationship off or what. Then you'll know. No more questions. No more doubts. Right? You can use our phone."

Phoebe had stared at the phone on the wall until it seemed like a huge red monster. To think that she could just walk over there and be talking to Griffin in less than two minutes was very tempting. But there had been no mistaking the finality of Griffin's good-bye.

Then Wes walked in, a bouquet of daffodils clasped in his hand. A pain stabbed Phoebe's heart as she watched Sasha fly into his arms. Phoebe realized how much she wanted a warm, giving relationship — if not with Griffin, then with someone else. But she knew there could never be anyone else as long as there was even a glimmer of hope Griffin might come back. Sasha was right. One more phone call couldn't cause her any more pain than she already felt. Get tough. Demand some answers. Phoebe stared at the phone some more and fingered the slip of paper with Griffin's number.

"Pheeb, we're going to slip down the street and get some ice-cream cones. Okay?" said Sasha.

"Only if you promise to get me a double dip of German chocolate," said Phoebe with a laugh.

"Sugar or regular cone?" called Wes, as they headed out the door.

"Whichever one will hold the most ice cream," shouted Phoebe. The door swung shut with a tinkle of the little bell. Phoebe flipped through a couple of big, glossy, coffee-table books. Everything she saw reminded her of Griffin — like the book on the history of Broadway musicals. Or the one of the wilderness areas of America; Griffin loved the outdoors. She could visualize him in every picture.

Phoebe glanced at the phone. It seemed to be mocking her. She looked away. Maybe she'd get him this book for his birthday. She slammed the book shut. She didn't even know when his birthday was. She didn't have an address to send it to. Grabbing the slip of paper, she marched to the phone and dialed the number.

"Yes, I'd like to speak to Griffin Neill, please," she said with determination when the bored voice answered the phone.

"He's not here."

Her confidence plummeted. "Ah, I see. Well, when do you expect him back?"

"Never."

Fear crept slowly up Phoebe's back. "Exactly what do you mean, never?"

"I mean, lady, he quit. Said he needed a vacation."

"Where did he go? Did he say? Do you know?" Phoebe could hear the panic in her voice.

"Look, lady. He's a big boy, okay? He does what he wants to do. I do what I want to do. He don't have to answer to me. I don't have to answer to him. I don't know where he is. I don't care where he is." The phone went dead.

Phoebe stared at the cone Sasha handed her. She hadn't heard them come in.

"Bad news?" asked Sasha quietly.

"I don't know," said Phoebe. "He quit his job. Went on vacation. No one knows anything about him."

"Gee, I'm sorry, Pheeb. Maybe it wasn't such a good idea to call. I just thought you needed some answers. I hate to see you getting all eaten up by this thing. You don't deserve it."

Phoebe smiled weakly. Good old Sasha. "No, you were right," she said. "I do need some answers. It just looks like I'm not going to get them."

"I sure hope this guy is worth it," said Wes.

"I think so," said Phoebe. "But I'm beginning to have my doubts. After all, I haven't seen him for months. Maybe I just dreamed him up. Maybe he's really a super jerk. I don't know anymore."

Sasha put her arm around Phoebe's shoulders. "Don't worry, Pheeb. We'll sort it out. I promise you."

"Yeah," added Wes. "Some of the guys at Leesberg are from New York. Maybe they can poke around when they go home for spring break. I'll ask them."

"Thanks a lot, you guys, I really appreciate all your help." Phoebe licked the drips from the sides of her cone. "I think I'll head on home. I told Mother I'd help with dinner. She's got some meeting tonight."

So she had been wrong — the pain could get worse, Phoebe thought as she trudged up the hill near her house. Well, at least I haven't fallen to pieces like I used to. Maybe all this is making me a stronger person. That certainly has to be for the good.

She walked along lost in thought, absent-mindedly avoiding the lines in the sidewalks. When she was little she thought fierce bears would rise up from underneath the slabs of concrete if she accidentally stepped on a line. Now she missed them automatically.

She turned the last corner to her street and stopped dead. Someone was coming down the road toward her. Someone who looked so much like Griffin Neill she could have sworn it was he. Lately she had begun to see him in every store and restaurant and office she was in, and it was getting pretty dark. Still, she continued to watch the figure get closer and closer. She squinted now to make out his face. She could not shake the eerie impression.

Then he began coming faster. Phoebe began walking more quickly, her heart pounding in her ears. The figure picked up speed, running full tilt toward her. Phoebe shrieked as they met in the middle of the road, first clinging together then spinning around and around.

"Griffin! Oh, Griffin!" sobbed Phoebe, holding him with all her strength.

"Phoebe! Beautiful Phoebe!" he said tenderly, his voice choked with emotion.

Phoebe was almost afraid to let him go — afraid he would disappear in the fog beginning to rise off the damp lawns all around them. She still couldn't believe he was real. Holding tightly onto his hand, she stepped back a couple of steps and stared up at him. Even in this half light she could see the familiar twinkle in his blue eyes, and his light brown hair caught the light from the shrouded street lamp. He was so beautiful, and so real. Phoebe flew into his arms again.

"I guess I have a few questions to answer, huh?" he said, burying his head in her hair.

"You're here! That's what's important. You're here! You don't have to explain anything," cried Phoebe.

"I want to. I owe you an explanation, and a huge apology. Please listen."

Phoebe wanted nothing more than to listen to him forever. His voice seemed to vibrate down into the very bottom of her soul and lift her spirits out into the light. She held his hand tightly as they walked along.

"Remember when I left," he began, his voice rich and low, "I told you I had been asked to try out for that play. The biggie. On Broadway. Well, I got the part."

"Oh, Griffin, that's wonderful!" exclaimed Phoebe, beaming up at him. She couldn't believe Griffin was with her, right beside her. The feel of his warm hand around hers was all the explanation she needed now.

"It was wonderful. For about three days. Knowing what kind of salary I would be making, I got a neat apartment down in Greenwich Village. Then I went to the first rehearsal." He sighed. "Only to be told my part had been given to someone else. Can you believe that?"

"Oh, Griffin! How could they do a thing like that?" Her heart ached for him.

"Unfortunately things like that happen all the time in the New York theater world. I was just naive when I first got there. You've got to prove yourself every minute, and still you can get dumped on. It's tough."

"Is it worth it?" asked Phoebe.

He gave her a tired smile that broke her heart. "I don't question that. I just know I want to be an actor and a good one. And New York's where it's all happening. I can't let it get me down." They walked along in silence, the fog wrapping them in its ever-thickening blanket, night dropping its dark curtain over the last light of day.

"So when I lost that part," continued Griffin, "my agent — Solomon — lost faith in me and dropped me. I had no job, no agent, and no place to live. Things were pretty shaky. That was just about the time you were planning to come up. I didn't know what to do. I wanted you to be proud of me." He paused and held her face in his hands. "Loving you kept me going through some really dark moments. But I didn't want you to see me down-and-out."

Phoebe wrapped her arm around his waist and put her head on his chest. These past months when she'd at least had her own warm room and good, home-cooked meals, Griffin was scratching out a miserable living in New York. If only she'd known. She couldn't bear the thought of him suffering like that. He was such an idealist, such a positive person, it must have been a terrible comedown.

"Finally I found a place to live with three other guys. All actors. Or maybe 'would-be actors' is a better term. A delightful apartment with armies of cockroaches to keep us company, one bedroom, the bathtub in the middle of the kitchen. . . ."

"The bathtub in the kitchen!" exclaimed Phoebe in horror. "Why?"

Griffin laughed. "So you can have a bath and cook your supper all at the same time. Sounds like fun, huh?"

"Ugh," said Phoebe, starting to laugh. "It sounds absolutely disgusting."

"Well, that's exactly why I didn't want you up there. It *was* disgusting. I didn't want you to see me living like that."

"But what about this job? The one in the photo studio. I called there again today."

"You did? What did they say?"

"That you'd gone. They didn't know where."

"Those jerks. I gave them a number where messages could be left." He turned Phoebe toward him again, resting his hands on her shoulders. "I know it doesn't seem like it, but your calls meant everything to me. I needed to know you loved me. I just didn't know how to love you back then. I felt like such a failure."

Phoebe held him tightly. She would have gone to visit him if he'd lived in a tent under the Brooklyn Bridge. If only she'd known how he felt, she would have just shown up. They could have worked things out from there. Anything was possible if they were together.

"Can't you get that job back?" she asked.

"I don't want it back," he said firmly. "I spent all day rolling up posters and shoving them into mailing tubes. The 'photo studio' was one of those places advertised in the back of comics — you know, where you get a picture of your favorite cat or friend blown up to poster size. Not exactly a class act."

Phoebe didn't care what he'd done. She was sad that things hadn't worked out the way he'd planned. He'd been so hopeful and excited about it all in the beginning. He'd obviously learned a few lessons the hard way. His pride had been crushed. It must have been really hard for him to come back to her like this and explain all the failures, but Phoebe didn't even think of them as failures. She admired his drive and dedication.

"Don't be so hard on yourself, Griffin," she said. "Acting's a competitive field. You can't expect to have things fall into place overnight."

"I know," he said plaintively. "That's what I'm learning. I've decided to get my high school diploma studying at night and during the day I've enrolled in a great drama school. I'll find another job." He kicked at the gravel at the side of the road. "I just want you to be proud of me."

Phoebe grabbed his face gently in her two hands. "Griffin, I've always been proud of you. I love you, remember? I know you're going to make it. I just know it. It'll take time. But I'll be here. Always. You can count on that."

He wrapped her slowly in his arms and found her mouth, his warmth and tenderness spreading through her. Phoebe gave herself up to the moment, knowing it would have to last a long, long time. Griffin would go back to New York. She'd go back to Kennedy High. They both had their lives to get on with, but they loved each other, and that was all that mattered. For now. Forever.

Coming Soon...
Couples #7
SWORN ENEMIES

Laurie squeezed some of the water out of her hair, and said, "Do I look as funny as you do?"

"Funnier," he replied. "I had a raincoat."

"It didn't do you much good, did it? You're soaked."

"Oh, no, I'm not. There's one spot under my left arm that's totally dry. Oops — I mean, that *was* totally dry." As Laurie put the car in gear and started out of the parking lot, he added, "Do I get to find out where we're going, or is this a mystery tour?"

"We're going to my house," said Laurie. "I owe you a couple of warm towels and some hot tea with honey. After that I'll bring you back to school or take you home, whatever you want. Okay?"

"Sure," he said, and settled back in his seat.

At the house, she led him upstairs to her father's dressing room and gave him two towels, and a big, white terry cloth robe. "Just put your things outside the door," she said. "As soon as I change I'll take them down and throw them in the dryer."

Laurie took two minutes to get out of her wet clothes and towel off, eight minutes to dry her hair, and at least five to decide what to put on next. She finally picked a pair of silk pants and a matching top in a soft peach color. She tied a red silk sash at the waist.

Tossing her head back to fluff her hair, she marched out of her room into the hall. The door to her dad's dressing room was open and the room was empty. As she stood at the head of the stairs, she thought of the silver in the dining room and wondered if she had let a burglar loose in the house. Then she heard someone whistling a cheery tune from the direction of the kitchen and relaxed. No burglar would go around whistling ragtime.

He was standing next to the stove holding a pile of wet clothes. The terry robe was a good fit. "I thought I'd save you some trouble," he said, "but I can't find the dryer."

"It's this way." She led him through the pantry into the laundry room, tossed the clothes in the dryer, and set it on auto, then went back to the kitchen and put two cups of water in the microwave. When she looked up, he was grinning at her. His slicked-down hair, beginning to fluff up as it dried, made him look like a little kid. "What's so funny?" she asked defensively.

"Do you always bake your water?"

"It's a lot faster this way. See? It's already hot."

"Hey, okay," he laughed. "I'm all in favor of progress."

Laurie found some cookies in a cabinet, spread them on a plate, and carried it into the media room.

He came close and took a cookie from the plate she was holding. Her pulse beat a little faster. "Is that all you want?" she asked, teasing him.

He smiled crookedly, deepening the dimple in his chin. "For now," he said.

Join the Team!

They're talented. They're fabulous-looking. They're winners! And they've got what you want! Don't miss any of these exciting CHEERLEADERS books!

ABSOLUTE SURRENDER

and Other Addresses

by
ANDREW MURRAY

MOODY PRESS • CHICAGO

ISBN: 0-8024-0560-6

46 47 Printing/LC/Year 87 86

Printed in the United States of America

CONTENTS

ABSOLUTE SURRRENDER

"And Ben-hadad the king of Syria gathered all his
host together: and there were thirty and two kings
with him, and horses, and chariots: and he went up
and besieged Samaria, and warred against it. And
he sent messengers to Ahab king of Israel into the
city, and said unto him, Thus saith Ben-hadad, Thy
silver and thy gold is mine; thy wives also and thy
children, even the goodliest, are mine. And the king
of Israel answered and said, My lord, O king, according to thy saying, I am thine and all that I have"
(I KINGS 20: 1-4).

WHAT BEN HADAD ASKED was absolute surrender; and
what Ahab gave was what was asked of him—absolute surrender. I want to use these words: "My
lord, O king, according to thy saying, I am thine, and
all that I have," as the words of absolute surrender
with which every child of God ought to yield himself
to his Father. We have heard it before, but we need
to hear it very definitely—the condition of God's
blessing is absolute surrender of all into His hands.
Praise God! If our hearts are willing for that, there is
no end to what God will do for us, and to the blessing
God will bestow.

Absolute surrender—let me tell you where I got

5

those words. I used them myself often, and you have
heard them numberless times. But in Scotland once I
was in a company where we were talking about the
condition of Christ's Church, and what the great
need of the Church and of believers is; and there
was in our company a godly worker who has much to
do in training workers, and I asked him what he
would say was the great need of the Church, and the
message that ought to be preached. He answered
very quietly and simply and determinedly:

"*Absolute surrender to God is the one thing.*"

The words struck me as never before. And that
man began to tell how, in the workers with whom he'
had to deal, he finds that if they are sound on that
point, even though they be backward, they are
willing to be taught and helped, and they always improve; whereas others who are not sound there very
often go back and leave the work. The condition for
obtaining God's full blessing is *absolute* surrender to
Him.

And now, I desire by God's grace to give to you
this message—that your God in Heaven answers the
prayers which you have offered for blessing on yourselves and for blessing on those around you by this
one demand: Are you willing to surrender yourselves
absolutely into His hands? What is our answer to
be? God knows there are hundreds of hearts who
have said it, and there are hundreds more who long
to say it but hardly dare to do so. And there are
hearts who have said it, but who have yet miserably
failed, and who feel themselves condemned because
they did not find the secret of the power to live that
life. May God have a word for all!

Let me say, first of all, that God claims it from us.

God Expects Your Surrender

Yes, it has its foundation in the very nature of God. God cannot do otherwise. Who is God? He is the Fountain of life, the only Source of existence and power and goodness, and throughout the universe there is nothing good but what God works. God has created the sun, and the moon, and the stars, and the flowers, and the trees, and the grass; and are they not all absolutely surrendered to God? Do they not allow God to work in them just what He pleases? When God clothes the lily with its beauty, is it not yielded up, surrendered, given over to God as He works in it its beauty? And God's redeemed children, oh, can you think that God can work His work if there is only half or a part of them surrendered? God cannot do it. God is life, and love, and blessing, and power, and infinite beauty, and God delights to communicate Himself to every child who is prepared to receive Him; but ah! this one lack of absolute surrender is just the thing that hinders God. And now He comes, and as God, He claims it.

You know in daily life what absolute surrender is. You know that everything has to be given up to its special, definite object and service. I have a pen in my pocket, and that pen is absolutely surrendered to the one work of writing, and that pen must be absolutely surrendered to my hand if I am to write properly with it. If another holds it partly, I cannot write properly. This coat is absolutely given up to me to cover my body. This building is entirely given up to religious services. And now, do you expect that in your immortal being, in the divine nature that you have received by regeneration, God can work His work, every day and every hour, unless you are entirely given up to Him? God cannot. The Temple of Solomon was absolutely surrendered to God when it was dedicated to Him. And every one of us is a temple of God, in which God will dwell and work mightily on one condition—absolute surrender to Him. God claims it, God is worthy of it, and without it God cannot work His blessed work in us.

God not only claims it, but God will work it Himself.

GOD ACCOMPLISHES YOUR SURRENDER

I am sure there is many a heart that says: "Ah, but that absolute surrender implies so much!" Someone says: "Oh, I have passed through so much trial and suffering, and there is so much of the self-life still remaining, and I dare not face the entire giving of it up, because I know it will cause so much trouble and agony."

Alas! alas! that God's children have such thoughts of Him, such cruel thoughts. Oh, I come to you with a message, fearful and anxious one. God does not ask you to give the perfect surrender in your strength, or by the power of your will; God is willing to work it in you. Do we not read: "It is God that worketh in us, both to will and to do of his good pleasure"? And that is what we should seek for—to go on our faces before God, until our hearts learn to believe that the everlasting God Himself will come in to turn out what is wrong, to conquer what is evil, and to work what is well-pleasing in His blessed sight. God Himself will work it in you.

Look at the men in the Old Testament, like Abraham. Do you think it was by accident that God found that man, the father of the faithful and the Friend of God, and that it was Abraham himself, apart from God, who had such faith and such obedience and such devotion? You know it is not so. God raised him up and prepared him as an instrument for His glory.

Did not God say to Pharaoh: "For this cause have I raised thee up, for to show in thee my power"?

And if God said that of him, will not God say it far more of every child of His?

Oh, I want to encourage you, and I want you to cast away every fear. Come with that feeble desire; and if there is the fear which says: "Oh, my desire is not strong enough, I am not willing for everything that may come, I do not feel bold enough to say I can conquer everything"—I pray you, learn to know and trust your God now. Say: "My God, I am willing that Thou shouldst make me willing." If there is anything holding you back, or any sacrifice you are afraid of making, come to God now, and prove how gracious your God is, and be not afraid that He will command from you what He will not bestow.

God comes and offers to work this absolute surrender in you. All these searchings and hungerings and longings that are in your heart, I tell you they are the drawings of the divine magnet, Christ Jesus. He lived a life of absolute surrender, He has possession of you; He is living in your heart by His Holy Spirit. You have hindered and hindered Him terribly, but He desires to help you to get hold of Him entirely. And He comes and draws you now by

His message and words. Will you not come and trust God to work in you that absolute surrender to Himself? Yes, blessed be God, He can do it, and He will do it.

God not only claims it and works it, but God accepts it when we bring it to Him.

GOD ACCEPTS YOUR SURRENDER

God works it in the secret of our heart, God urges us by the hidden power of His Holy Spirit to come and speak it out, and we have to bring and to yield to Him that absolute surrender. But remember, when you come and bring God that absolute surrender, it may, as far as your feelings or your consciousness go, be a thing of great imperfection, and you may doubt and hesitate and say:

"Is it absolute?"

But, oh, remember there was once a man to whom Christ had said:

"If thou canst believe, all things are possible to him that believeth."

And his heart was afraid, and he cried out:

"Lord, I believe, help thou mine unbelief."

That was a faith that triumphed over the Devil, and the evil spirit was cast out. And if you come and say: "Lord, I yield myself in absolute surrender to my God," even though it be with a trembling heart and with the consciousness: "I do not feel the power, I do not feel the determination, I do not feel the assurance," it will succeed. Be not afraid, but come just as you are, and even in the midst of your trembling the power of the Holy Ghost will work.

Have you never yet learned the lesson that the Holy Ghost works with mighty power, while on the human side everything appears feeble? Look at the Lord Jesus Christ in Gethsemane. We read that He, "through the eternal Spirit," offered Himself a sacrifice unto God. The Almighty Spirit of God was enabling Him to do it. And yet what agony and fear and exceeding sorrow came over Him, and how He prayed! Externally, you can see no sign of the mighty power of the Spirit, but the Spirit of God was there. And even so, while you are feeble and fighting and trembling, in faith in the hidden work of God's Spirit do not fear, but yield yourself.

And when you do yield yourself in absolute surrender, let it be in the faith that God does now accept of it. That is the great point, and that is what we so often miss—that believers should be thus occupied with God in this matter of surrender. I pray you, be occupied with God. We want to get help, every one of us, so that in our daily life God shall be clearer to us, God shall have the right place, and be "all in all." And if we are to have that through life, let us begin now and look away from ourselves, and look up to God. Let each believe—while I, a poor worm on earth and a trembling child of God, full of failure and sin and fear, bow here, and no one knows what passes through my heart, and while I in simplicity say, O God, I accept Thy terms; I have pleaded for blessing on myself and others, I have accepted Thy terms of absolute surrender—while your heart says that in deep silence, remember there is a God present that takes note of it, and writes it down in His book, and there is a God present who at that very moment takes possession of you. You may not feel it, you may not realize it, but God takes possession if you will trust Him.

God not only claims it, and works it, and accepts it when I bring it, but God maintains it.

God Maintains Your Surrender

That is the great difficulty with many. People say: "I have often been stirred at a meeting, or at a convention, and I have consecrated myself to God, but it has passed away. I know it may last for a week or for a month, but away it fades, and after a time it is all gone."

But listen! It is because you do not believe what I am now going to tell you and remind you of. When God has begun the work of absolute surrender in you, and when God has accepted your surrender, then God holds Himself bound to care for it and to keep it. Will you believe that?

In this matter of surrender there are two: God and I—I a worm, God the everlasting and omnipotent Jehovah. Worm, will you be afraid to trust yourself to this mighty God now? God is willing. Do you not believe that He can keep you continually, day by day, and moment by moment?

> Moment by moment I'm *kept* in His love;
> Moment by moment I've life from above.

If God allows the sun to shine upon you moment by moment, without intermission, will not God let His life shine upon you every moment? And why have

you not experienced it? Because you have not
trusted God for it, and you do not surrender yourself
absolutely to God in that trust.

A life of absolute surrender has its difficulties. I
do not deny that. Yes, it has something far more than
difficulties: it is a life that with men is absolutely impossible. But by the grace of God, by the power of
God, by the power of the Holy Spirit dwelling in us, it
is a life to which we are destined, and a life that is
possible for us, praise God! Let us believe that God
will maintain it.

Some of you have read the words of that aged
saint who, on his ninetieth birthday, told of all God's
goodness to him—I mean George Muller. What did
he say he believed to be the secret of his happiness,
and of all the blessing which God had given him? He
said he believed there were two reasons. The one
was that he had been enabled by grace to maintain a
good conscience before God day by day; the other
was, that he was a lover of God's Word. Ah, yes, a
good conscience is complete obedience to God day by
day, and fellowship with God every day in His Word,
and prayer—that is a life of absolute surrender.

Such a life has two sides—on the one side, absolute surrender to work what God wants you to do;
on the other side, to let God work what He wants to
do.

First, *to do what God wants you to do.*

Give up yourselves absolutely to the will of God.
You know something of that will; not enough, far
from all. But say absolutely to the Lord God: "By Thy
grace I desire to do Thy will in everything, every

moment of every day." Say: "Lord God, not a word upon my tongue but for Thy glory, not a movement of my temper but for Thy glory, not an affection of love or hate in my heart but for Thy glory, and according to Thy blessed will."

Someone says: "Do you think that possible?"

I ask, What has God promised you, and what can God do to fill a vessel absolutely surrendered to Him? Oh, God wants to bless you in a way beyond what you expect. From the beginning, ear hath not heard, neither hath the eye seen, what God hath prepared for them that wait for Him. God has prepared unheard-of-things, blessings much more wonderful than you can imagine, more mighty than you can conceive. They are divine blessings. Oh, say now:

"I give myself absolutely to God, to His will, to do only what God wants."

It is God who will enable you to carry out the surrender.

And, on the other side, come and say: "I give myself absolutely to God, *to let Him work in me to will and to do of His good pleasure*, as He has promised to do."

Yes, the living God wants to work in His children in a way that we cannot understand, but that God's Word has revealed, and He wants to work in us every moment of the day. God is willing to maintain our life. Only let our absolute surrender be one of simple, childlike, and unbounded trust.

GOD BLESSES WHEN YOU SURRENDER

This absolute surrender to God will wonderfully bless.

What Ahab said to his enemy, King Ben-hadad—"My lord, O king, according to thy word I am thine, and all that I have"—shall we not say to our God and loving Father? If we do say it, God's blessing will come upon us. God wants us to be separate from the world; we are called to come out from the world that hates God. Come out for God, and say: "Lord, anything for Thee." If you say that with prayer, and speak that into God's ear, He will accept it, and He will teach you what it means.

I say again, God will bless you. You have been praying for blessing. But do remember, there must be absolute surrender. At every tea-table you see it. Why is tea poured into that cup? Because it is empty, and given up for the tea. But put ink, or vinegar, or wine into it, and will they pour the tea into the vessel? And can God fill you, can God bless you if you are not absolutely surrendered to Him? He cannot. Let us believe God has wonderful blessings for us, if we will but stand up for God, and say, be it with a trembling will, yet with a believing heart:

"O God, I accept Thy demands. I am thine and all that I have. Absolute surrender is what my soul yields to Thee by divine grace."

You may not have such strong and clear feelings of deliverances as you would desire to have, but humble yourselves in His sight, and acknowledge that you have grieved the Holy Spirit by your self-will, self-confidence, and self-effort. Bow humbly before him in the confession of that, and ask him to break the heart and to bring you into the dust before Him. Then, as you bow before Him, just accept God's teaching that in your flesh "there dwelleth no good thing," and that nothing will help you except another life which must come in. You must deny self once for all. Denying self must every moment be the power of your life, and then Christ will come in and take possession of you.

When was Peter delivered? When was the change accomplished? The change began with Peter weeping, and the Holy Ghost came down and filled his heart.

God the Father loves to give us the power of the Spirit. We have the Spirit of God dwelling within us. We come to God confessing that, and praising God for it, and yet confessing how we have grieved the Spirit. And then we bow our knees to the Father to ask that He would strengthen us with all might by the Spirit in the inner man, and that He would fill us with His mighty power. And as the Spirit reveals Christ to us, Christ comes to live in our hearts forever, and the self-life is cast out.

Let us bow before God in humility, and in that humility confess before Him the state of the whole Church. No words can tell the sad state of the Church of Christ on earth. I wish I had words to speak what I sometimes feel about it. Just think of the Christians around you. I do not speak of nominal Christians, or of professing Christians, but I speak of hundreds and thousands of honest, earnest Christians who are not living a life in the power of God or to His glory. So little power, so little devotion or consecration to God, so little perception of the truth that a Christian is a man utterly surrendered to God's will! Oh, we want to confess the sins of God's people around us, and to humble ourselves.

We are members of that sickly body, and the sickliness of the body will hinder us, and break us down, unless we come to God, and in confession separate ourselves from partnership with worldliness, with coldness toward each other, unless we give up ourselves to be entirely and wholly for God.

How much Christian work is being done in the spirit of the flesh and in the power of self! How much work, day by day, in which human energy—our will and our thoughts about the work—is continually manifested, and in which there is but little of waiting upon God, and upon the power of the Holy Ghost! Let us make confession. But as we confess the state of the Church and the feebleness and sinfulness of work for God among us, let us come back to ourselves. Who is there who truly longs to be delivered from the power of the self-life, who truly acknowledges that it *is* the power of self and the flesh, and who is willing to cast all at the feet of Christ? There is deliverance.

I heard of one who had been an earnest Christian, and who spoke about the "cruel" thought of separation and death. But you do not think that, do you? What are we to think of separation and death? This: death was the path to glory for Christ. For the joy set before Him He endured the cross. The cross was the birthplace of His everlasting glory. Do you love Christ? Do you long to be *in* Christ, and not *like* Him? Let death be to you the most desirable thing on earth—death to self, and fellowship with Christ. Separation—do you think it a hard thing to be called to be entirely free from the world, and by that

separation to be united to God and His love, by
separation to become prepared for living and
walking with God every day? Surely one ought to
say:

"Anything to bring me to separation, to death, for
a life of full fellowship with God and Christ."

Come and cast this self-life and flesh-life at the
feet of Jesus. Then trust Him. Do not worry yourselves with trying to understand all about it, but
come in the living faith that Christ will come into you
with the power of His death and the power of His
life; and then the Holy Spirit will bring the whole
Christ—Christ crucified and risen and living in
glory—into your heart.

"THE FRUIT OF THE SPIRIT IS LOVE"

I WANT TO LOOK at the fact of a life filled with the Holy Spirit more from the practical side, and to show how this life will show itself in our daily walk and conduct.

Under the Old Testament you know the Holy Spirit often came upon men as a divine Spirit of revelation to reveal the mysteries of God, or for power to do the work of God. But He did not then dwell in them. Now, many just want the Old Testament gift of power for work, but know very little of the New Testament gift of the indwelling Spirit, animating and renewing the whole life. When God gives the Holy Spirit, His great object is the formation of a holy character. It is a gift of a holy mind and spiritual disposition, and what we need above everything else, is to say:

"I must have the Holy Spirit sanctifying my whole inner life if I am really to live for God's glory."

You might say that when Christ promised the Spirit to the disciples, He did so that they might have power to be witnesses. True, but then they received the Holy Ghost in such heavenly power and reality that He took possession of their whole being at once and so fitted them as holy men for doing the work with power as they had to do it. Christ spoke of power to the disciples, but it was the Spirit filling their whole being that worked the power.

I wish now to dwell upon the passage found in Galatians 5:22:

"The fruit of the Spirit is love."

We read that "Love is the fulfilling of the law," and my desire is to speak on love as a fruit of the Spirit with a twofold object. One is that this word may be a searchlight in our hearts, and give us a test by which to try all our thoughts about the Holy Spirit and all our experience of the holy life. Let us try ourselves by this word. Has this been our daily habit, to seek the being filled with the Holy Spirit as the Spirit of love? "The fruit of the Spirit is love." Has it been our experience that the more we have of the Holy Spirit the more loving we become? In claiming the Holy Spirit we should make this the first object of our expectation. The Holy Spirit comes as a Spirit of love.

Oh, if this were true in the Church of Christ how different her state would be! May God help us to get hold of this simple, heavenly truth that the fruit of the Spirit is a love which appears in the life, and that just as the Holy Spirit gets real possession of the life, the heart will be filled with real, divine, universal love.

One of the great causes why God cannot bless His Church is *the want of love*. When the body is divided, there cannot be strength. In the time of their great religious wars, when Holland stood out so nobly against Spain, one of their mottoes was: "Unity gives strength." It is only when God's people stand as one body, one before God in the fellowship of love, one toward another in deep affection, one before the world in a love that the world can see—it is only then that they will have power to secure the blessing which they ask of God. Remember that if a vessel that ought to be one whole is cracked into many pieces, it cannot be filled. You can take a potsherd, one part of a vessel, and dip out a little water into that, but if you want the vessel full, the vessel must be whole. That is literally true of Christ's Church, and if there is one thing we must pray for still, it is this: Lord, melt us together into one by the power of the Holy Spirit; let the Holy Spirit, who at Pentecost made them all of one heart and one soul, do His blessed work among us. Praise God, we can love each other in a divine love, for "the fruit of the Spirit is love." Give yourselves up to love, and the Holy Spirit will come; receive the Spirit, and He will teach you to love more.

GOD IS LOVE

Now, why is it that the fruit of the Spirit is love? *Because God is love.*

And what does that mean?

It is the very nature and being of God to delight in communicating Himself. God has no selfishness, God keeps nothing to Himself. God's nature is to be always giving. In the sun and the moon and the stars, in every flower you see it, in every bird in the air, in every fish in the sea. God communicates life to His creatures. And the angels around His throne, the seraphim and cherumbim who are flames of fire—whence have they their glory? It is because

God is love, and He imparts to them of His brightness and His blessedness. And we, His redeemed children—God delights to pour His love into us. And why? Because, as I said, God keeps nothing for Himself. From eternity God had His only begotten Son, and the Father gave Him all things, and nothing that God had was kept back. "God is love."

One of the old Church fathers said that we cannot better understand the Trinity than as a revelation of divine love—the Father, the loving One, the Fountain of love; the Son, the beloved one, the Reservior of love, in whom the love was poured out; and the Spirit, the living love that united both and then overflowed into this world. The Spirit of Pentecost, the Spirit of the Father, and the Spirit of the Son is love. And when the Holy Spirit comes to us and to other men, will He be less a Spirit of love than He is in God? It cannot be; He cannot change His nature. The Spirit of God is love, and "the fruit of the Spirit is love."

MANKIND NEEDS LOVE

Why is that so? That was the one great need of mankind, that was the thing which Christ's redemption came to accomplish: *to restore love to this world.*

When man sinned, why was it that he sinned? Selfishness triumphed—he sought self instead of God. And just look! Adam at once begins to accuse the woman of having led him astray. Love to God had gone, love to man was lost. Look again: of the first two children of Adam the one becomes a murderer of his brother.

Does not that teach us that sin had robbed the world of love? Ah! what a proof the history of the world has been of love having been lost! There may have been beautiful examples of love even among the heathen, but only as a little remnant of what was lost. One of the worst things sin did for man was to make him selfish, for selfishness cannot love.

The Lord Jesus Christ came down from Heaven as the Son of God's love. "God so loved the world that He gave His only begotten Son." God's Son came to show what love is, and He lived a life of love here upon earth in fellowship with His disciples, in compassion over the poor and miserable, in love even to His enemies, and He died the death of love. And when He went to Heaven, whom did He send down? The Spirit of love, to come and banish selfishness and envy and pride, and bring the love of God into the hearts of men. "The fruit of the Spirit is love."

And what was the preparation for the promise of the Holy Spirit? You know that promise as found in the fourteenth chapter of John's Gospel. But remember what precedes in the thirteenth chapter. Before Christ promised the Holy Spirit, He gave a new commandment, and about that new commandment He said wonderful things. One thing was: "Even as I have loved you, so love ye one another." To them His dying love was to be the only law of their conduct and intercourse with each other. What a message to those fishermen, to those men full of pride and selfishness! "Learn to love each other," said Christ, "as I have loved you." And by the grace of God they

did it. When Pentecost came, they were of one heart
and one soul. Christ did it for them.

And now He calls us to dwell and to walk in love.
He demands that though a man hate you, still you
love him. True love cannot be conquered by anything
in Heaven or upon the earth. The more hatred there
is, the more love triumphs through it all and shows
its true nature. This is the love that Christ commanded His disciples to exercise.

What more did He say? "By this shall all men
know that ye are my disciples, if ye have love one to
another."

You all know what it is to wear a badge. And
Christ said to His disciples in effect: "I give you a
badge, and that badge is love. That is to be your
mark. It is the only thing in Heaven or on earth by
which men can know me."

Do we not begin to fear that love has fled from
the earth? That if we were to ask the world: "Have
you seen us wear the badge of love?" the world
would say: "No; what we have heard of the Church
of Christ is that there is not a place where there is no
quarreling and separation." Let us ask God with one
heart that we may wear the badge of Jesus' love. God
is able to give it.

LOVE CONQUERS SELFISHNESS

"The fruit of the Spirit is love." Why? Because
*nothing but love can expel and conquer our
selfishness.*

Self is the great curse, whether in its relation to
God, or to our fellow-men in general, or to fellow-
Christians, thinking of ourselves and seeking our

own. Self is our greatest curse. But, praise God, Christ came to redeem us from self. We sometimes talk about deliverance from the self-life—and thank God for every word that can be said about it to help us—but I am afraid some people think deliverance from the self-life means that now they are going to have no longer any trouble in serving God; and they forget that deliverance from self-life means to be a vessel overflowing with love to everybody all the day.

And there you have the reason why many people pray for the power of the Holy Ghost, and they get something, but oh, so little! because they prayed for power for work, and power for blessing, but they have not prayed for power for full deliverance from self. That means not only the righteous self in intercourse with God, but the unloving self in intercourse with men. And there is deliverance. "The fruit of the Spirit is love." I bring you the glorious promise of Christ that He is able to fill our hearts with love.

A great many of us try hard at times to love. We try to force ourselves to love, and I do not say that is wrong; it is better than nothing. But the end of it is always very sad. "I fail continually," such as one must confess. And what is the reason? The reason is simply this: Because they have never learned to believe and accept the truth that the Holy Spirit can pour God's love into their heart. That blessed text; often it has been limited!—"The love of God is shed abroad in our hearts." It has often been understood in this sense: It means the love of God *to me.* Oh, what a limitation! That is only the beginning. The

love of God is always the love of God in its entirety,
in its fullness as an indwelling power, a love of God
to me that leaps back to Him in love, and overflows
to my fellow-men in love—God's love to me, and my
love to God, and my love to my fellow-men. The three
are one; you cannot separate them.

Do believe that the love of God can be shed abroad
in your heart and mine so that we can love all the
day.

"Ah!" you say, "how little I have understood
that!"

Why is a lamb always gentle? Because that is its
nature. Does it cost the lamb any trouble to be gentle? No. Why not? It is so beautiful and gentle. Has a
lamb to study to be gentle? No. Why does that come
so easy? It is its nature. And a wolf—why does it
cost a wolf no trouble to be cruel, and to put its fangs
into the poor lamb or sheep? Because that is its
nature. It has not to summon up its courage; the
wolf-nature is there.

And how can I learn to love? Never until the Spirit
of God fills my heart with God's love, and I begin to
long for God's love in a very different sense from
which I have sought it so selfishly, as a comfort and
a joy and a happiness and a pleasure to myself;
never until I begin to learn that "God is love," and to
claim it, and receive it as an indwelling power for
self-sacrifice; never until I begin to see that my
glory, my blessedness, is to be like God and like
Christ, in giving up everything in myself for my
fellow-men. May God teach us that! Oh, the divine
blessedness of the love with which the Holy Spirit
can fill our hearts! "The fruit of the Spirit is love."

LOVE IS GOD'S GIFT

Once again I ask, Why must this be so? And my answer is: *Without this we cannot live the daily life of love.*

How often, when we speak about the consecrated life, we have to speak about *temper*, and some people have sometimes said:

"You make too much of temper."

I do not think we can make too much of it. Think for a moment of a clock and of what its hands mean. The hands tell me what is within the clock, and if I see that the hands stand still, or that the hands point wrong, or that the clock is slow or fast, I say that something inside the clock is not working properly. And temper is just like the revelation that the clock gives of what is within. Temper is a proof whether the love of Christ is filling the heart, or not. How many there are who find it easier in church, or in prayer-meeting, or in work for the Lord—diligent, earnest work—to be holy and happy than in the daily life with wife and children and servant; easier to be holy and happy outside the home than in it! Where is the love of God? In Christ. God has prepared for us a wonderful redemption in Christ, and He longs to make something supernatural of us. Have we learned to long for it, and ask for it, and expect it in its fullness?

Then there is the *tongue!* We sometimes speak of the tongue when we talk of the better life, and the restful life, but just think what liberty many Christians give to their tongues. They say:

"I have a right to think what I like."

When they speak about each other, when they speak about their neighbors, when they speak about other Christians, how often there are sharp remarks! God keep me from saying anything that would be unloving; God shut my mouth if I am not to speak in tender love. But what I am saying is a fact. How often there are found among Christians who are banded together in work, sharp criticism, sharp judgment, hasty opinion, unloving words, secret contempt of each other, secret condemnation of each other! Oh, just as a mother's love covers her children and delights in them and has the tenderest compasssion with their foibles or failures, so there ought to be in the heart of every believer a motherly love toward every brother and sister in Christ. Have you aimed at that? Have you sought it? Have you ever pleaded for it? Jesus Christ said: "As I have loved you . . . love one another." And He did not put that among the other commandments, but He said in effect:

"That is a NEW commandment, the one commandment: Love one another as I have loved you."

It is in our daily life and conduct that the fruit of the Spirit is love. From that there comes all the graces and virtues in which love is manifested: joy, peace, longsuffering, gentleness, goodness; no sharpness or hardness in your tone, no unkindness or selfishness; meekness before God and man. You see that all these are the gentler virtues. I have often thought as I read those words in Colossians, "Put on therefore as the elect of God, holy and beloved, bowels of mercies, kindness, humbleness of mind, meekness, longsuffering," that if we had written, we should have put in the foreground the manly virtues, such as zeal, courage and diligence; but we need to see how the gentler, the most womanly virtues are specially connected with dependence upon the Holy Spirit. These are indeed heavenly graces. They never were found in the heathen world. Christ was needed to come from Heaven to teach us. Your blessedness is longsuffering, meekness, kindness; your glory is humility before God. The fruit of the Spirit that He brought from Heaven out of the heart of the crucified Christ, and that He gives in our heart, is first and foremost—love.

You know what John says: "No man hath seen God at any time. If we love one another, God dwelleth in us." That is, I cannot see God, but as a compensation I can see my brother, and if I love him, God dwells in me. Is that really true? That I cannot see God, but I must love my brother, and God will dwell in me? Loving my brother is the way to real fellowship with God. You know what John further says in that most solemn test, "If a man say, I love God, and hateth his brother, he is a liar; for he that loveth not his brother whom he hath seen, how can he love God whom he hath not seen?" (I John 4:20). There is a brother, a most unlovable man. He worries you every time you meet him. He is of the very opposite disposition to yours. You are a careful businessman, and you have to do with him in your business. He is most untidy, unbusiness-like. You say:

"I cannot love him."

Oh, friend, you have not learned the lesson that Christ wanted to teach above everything. Let a man be what he will, you are to love him. Love is to be the fruit of the Spirit all the day and every day. Yes, listen! if a man loves not his brother whom he hath seen—if you don't love that unlovable man whom you have seen, how can you love God whom you have not seen? You can deceive yourself with beautiful thoughts about loving God. You must prove your love to God by your love to your brother; that is the one standard by which God will judge your love to Him. If the love of God is in your heart you will love your brother. The fruit of the Spirit is love.

And what is the reason that God's Holy Spirit cannot come in power? Is it not possible?

You remember the comparison I used in speaking of the vessel. I can dip a little water into a potsherd, a bit of a vessel; but if a vessel is to be full, it must be unbroken. And the children of God, wherever they come together, to whatever church or mission or society they belong, must love each other intensely, or the Spirit of God cannot do His work. We talk about grieving the Spirit of God by worldliness and ritualism and formality and error and indifference, but, I tell you, the one thing above everything that grieves God's Spirit is this want of love. Let every heart search itself, and ask that God may search it.

Our Love Shows God's Power

Why are we taught that "the fruit of the Spirit is love"? *Because the Spirit of God has come to make our daily life an exhibition of divine power and a revelation of what God can do for His children.*

In the second and the fourth chapters of Acts we read that the disciples were of one heart and of one soul. During the three years they had walked with Christ they never had been in that spirit. All Christ's teaching could not make them of one heart and one soul. But the Holy Spirit came from Heaven and shed the love of God in their hearts, and they were of one heart and one soul. The same Holy Spirit that brought the love of Heaven into their hearts must fill us too. Nothing less will do. Even as Christ did, one might preach love for three years with the tongue of an angel, but that would not teach any man to love unless the power of the Holy Spirit should come upon him to bring the love of Heaven into his heart.

Think of the church at large. What divisions! Think of the different bodies. Take the question of holiness, take the question of the cleansing blood, take the question of the baptism of the Spirit—what differences are caused among dear believers by such questions! That there are differences of opinion does not trouble me. We do not have the same constitution and temperament and mind. But how often hate, bitterness, contempt, separation, unlovingness are caused by the holiest truths of God's Word! Our doctrines, our creeds, have been more important than love. We often think we are valiant for the truth and we forget God's command to speak the truth in love. And it was so in the time of the Reformation between the Lutheran and Calvinistic churches. What bitterness there was than in regard to the Holy Supper, which was meant to be the bond of union among all believers! And so, down the ages, the very dearest truths of God have become mountains that have separated us.

If we want to pray in power, and if we want to expect the Holy Spirit to come down in power, and if
we want indeed that God shall pour out His Spirit,
we must enter into a covenant with God that we love
one another with a heavenly love.

Are you ready for that? Only that is true love that
is large enough to take in all God's children, the most
unloving and unlovable, and unworthy, and unbearable, and trying. If my vow—absolute surrender to God—was true, then it must mean absolute
surrender to the divine love to fill me; to be a servant
of love to love every child of God around me. "The
fruit of the Spirit is love."

Oh, God did something wonderful when He gave
Christ, at His right hand, the Holy Spirit to come
down out of the heart of the Father and His
everlasting love. And how we have degraded the
Holy Spirit into a mere power by which we have to
do our work! God forgive us! Oh, that the Holy Spirit
might be held in honor as a power to fill us with the
very life and nature of God and of Christ!

CHRISTIAN WORK REQUIRES LOVE

"The fruit of the Spirit is love." I ask once again,
Why is it so? And the answer comes: *That is the only
power in which Christians really can do their work.*

Yes, it is that we need. We want not only love that
is to bind us to each other, but we want a divine love
in our work for the lost around us. Oh, do we not often undertake a great deal of work, just as men undertake work of philanthropy, from a natural spirit
of compassion for our fellow-men? Do we not often

undertake Christian work because our minister or friend calls us to it? And do we not often perform Christian work with a certain zeal but without having had a baptism of love?

People often ask: "What is the baptism of fire?"

I have answered more than once: I know no fire like the fire of God, the fire of everlasting love that consumed the sacrifice on Calvary. The baptism of love is what the Church needs, and to get that we must begin at once to get down upon our faces before God in confession, and plead:

"Lord, let love from Heaven flow down into my heart. I am giving up my life to pray and live as one who has given himself up for the everlasting love to dwell in and fill him."

Ah, yes, if the love of God were in our hearts, what a difference it would make! There are hundreds of believers who say:

"I work for Christ, and I feel I could work much harder, but I have not the gift. I do not know how or where to begin. I do not know what I can do."

Brother, sister, ask God to baptize you with the Spirit of love, and love will find its way. Love is a fire that will burn through every difficulty. You may be a shy, hesitating man, who cannot speak well, but love can burn through everything. God fill us with love! We need it for our work.

You have read many a touching story of love expressed, and you have said, How beautiful! I heard one not long ago. A lady had been asked to speak at a Rescue Home where there were a number of poor women. As she arrived there and got to the window with the matron, she saw outside a wretched object sitting, and asked:

"Who is that?"

The matron answered: "She has been into the house thirty or forty times, and she has always gone away again. Nothing can be done with her, she is so low and hard."

But the lady said: "She must come in."

The matron then said: "We have been waiting for you, and the company is assembled, and you have only an hour for the address."

The lady replied: "No, this is of more importance"; and she went outside where the woman was sitting and said:

"My sister, what is the matter?"

"I am not your sister," was the reply.

Then the lady laid her hand on her, and said: "Yes, I am your sister, and I love you"; and so she spoke until the heart of the poor woman was touched.

The conversation lasted some time, and the company were waiting patiently. Ultimately the lady brought the woman into the room. There was the poor wretched, degraded creature, full of shame. She would not sit on a chair, but sat down on a stool beside the speaker's seat, and she let her lean against her, with her arms around the poor woman's neck, while she spoke to the assembled people. And that love touched the woman's heart; she had found one who really loved her, and that love gave access to the love of Jesus.

Praise God! there is love upon earth in the hearts of God's children; but oh, that there were more!

O God, baptize our ministers with a tender love, and our missionaries, and our colporters, and our Bible-readers, and our workers, and our young men's and young women's associations. Oh, that God would begin with us now, and baptize us with heavenly love!

LOVE INSPIRES INTERCESSION

Once again. *It is only love that can fit us for the work of intercession.*

I have said that love must fit us for our work. Do you know what the hardest and the most important work is that has to be done for this sinful world? It is the work of intercession, the work of going to God and taking time to lay hold on Him.

A man may be an earnest Christian, an earnest minister, and a man may do good, but alas! how often he has to confess that he knows but little of what it is to tarry with God. May God give us the great gift of an intercessory spirit, a spirit of prayer and supplication! Let me ask you in the name of Jesus not to let a day pass without praying for all saints, and for all God's people.

I find there are Christians who think little of that. I find there are prayer unions where they pray for the members, and not for all believers. I pray you, take time to pray for the Church of Christ. It is right to pray for the heathen, as I have already said. God help us to pray more for them. It is right to pray for missionaries and for evangelistic work, and for the unconverted. But Paul did not tell people to pray for the heathen or the unconverted. Paul told them to pray for believers. Do make this your first prayer every day: "Lord, bless Thy saints everywhere."

The state of Christ's Church is indescribably low. Plead for God's people that He would visit them, plead for each other, plead for all believers who are trying to work for God. Let love fill your heart. Ask Christ to pour it out afresh into you every day. Try to get it into you by the Holy Spirit of God: I am separated unto the Holy Spirit, and the fruit of the Spirit is love. God help us to understand it.

May God grant that we learn day by day to wait more quietly upon Him. Do not wait upon God only for ourselves, or the power to do so will soon be lost; but give ourselves up to the ministry and the love of intercession, and pray more for God's people, for God's people round about us, for the Spirit of love in ourselves and in them, and for the work of God we are connected with; and the answer will surely come, and our waiting upon God will be a source of untold blessing and power. "The fruit of the Spirit is love."

Have you a lack of love to confess before God? Then make confession and say before Him, "O Lord, my lack of heart, my lack of love—I confess it." And then, as you cast that lack at His feet, believe that the blood cleanses you, that Jesus comes in His mighty, cleansing, saving power to deliver you, and that He will give His Holy Spirit.

"THE FRUIT OF THE SPIRIT IS LOVE"

SEPARATED UNTO THE
HOLY GHOST

*"Now there were in the church that was at An-
tioch certain prophets and teachers; as Barnabas,
and Simeon that was called Niger, and Lucius of
Cyrene, and Manaen . . . and Saul.*

*"As they ministered to the Lord, and fasted, the
Holy Ghost said, Separate me Barnabas and Saul for
the work whereunto I have called them.*

*"And when they had fasted and prayed, and laid
their hands on them, they sent them away. So they,
being sent forth by the Holy Ghost, departed unto
Seleucia"* (ACTS 13:1-4).

IN THE STORY of our text we shall find some precious
thoughts to guide us as to what God would have of
us, and what God would do for us. The great lesson
of the verses quoted is this: *The Holy Ghost is the
director of the work of God upon the earth.* And what
we should do if we are to work rightly for God, and if
God is to bless our work, is to see that we stand in a
right relation to the Holy Ghost, that we give Him
every day the place of honor that belongs to Him,
and that in all our work and (what is more) in all our
private inner life, the Holy Ghost shall always have
the first place. Let me point out to you some of the
precious thoughts our passage suggests.

First of all, we see that *God has His own plans with regard to His kingdom.*

His church at Antioch had been established. God had certain plans and intentions with regard to Asia, and with regard to Europe. He had conceived them; they were His, and He made them known to His servants.

Our great Commander organizes every campaign, and His generals and officers do not always know the great plans. They often receive sealed orders, and they have to wait on Him for what He gives them as orders. God in Heaven has wishes, and a will, in regard to any work that ought to be done, and to the way in which it has to be done. Blessed is the man who gets into God's secrets and works under God.

Some years ago, at Wellington, South Africa, where I live, we opened a Mission Institute—what is counted there a fine large building. At our opening services the principal said something that I have never forgotten. He remarked:

"Last year we gathered here to lay the foundation-stone, and what was there then to be seen? Nothing but rubbish, and stones, and bricks, and ruins of an old building that had been pulled down. There we laid the foundation-stone, and very few knew what the building was that was to rise. No one know it perfectly in every detail except one man, the architect. In his mind it was all clear, and as the contractor and the mason and the carpenter came to their work they took their orders from him, and the humblest laborer had to be obedient to orders, and the structure rose, and this beautiful building has been completed. And just so," he added, "this building that we open today is but laying the foundation of a work of which only God knows what is to become."

But God has His workers and His plans clearly mapped out, and our position is to wait, that God should communicate to us as much of His will as each time is needful.

We have simply to be faithful in obedience, carrying out His orders. God has a plan for His Church upon earth. But alas! we too often make our plan, and we think that we know what ought to be done. We ask God first to bless our feeble efforts, instead of absolutely refusing to go unless God go before us. God has planned for the work and the extension of His kingdom. The Holy Ghost has had that work given in charge to Him. "The work whereunto I have called them." May God, therefore, help us all to be afraid of touching "the ark of God" except as we are led by the Holy Ghost.

Then the second thought—*God is willing and able to reveal to His servants what His will is.*

Yes, blessed be God, communications still come down from Heaven! As we read here what the Holy Ghost said, so the Holy Ghost will still speak to His Church and His people. In these later days He has often done it. He has come to individual men, and by His divine teaching He has led them out into fields of labor that others could not at first understand or approve, into ways and methods that did not recommend themselves to the majority. But the Holy Ghost does still in our time teach His people. Thank God, in our foreign missionary societies and in our home missions, and in a thousand forms of work, the guiding of the Holy Ghost is known, but (we are all ready, I think, to confess) *too little* known. We have not learned enough to wait upon Him, and so we should make a solemn declaration before God: O God, we want to wait more for Thee to show us Thy will.

Do not ask God only for power. Many a Christian has his own plan of working, but God must send the power. The man works in his own will, and God must give the grace—the one reason why God often gives so little grace and so little success. But let us all take our place before God and say:

"What is done in the will of God the strength of God will not be withheld from it; what is done in the will of God must have the mighty blessing of God."

And so let our first desire be to have the will of God revealed.

If you ask me, Is it an easy thing to get these communications from Heaven, and to understand them? I can give you the answer. It is easy to those who are in right fellowship with Heaven, and who understand the art of waiting upon God in prayer.

How often we ask: How can a person know the will of God? And people want, when they are in perplexity, to pray very earnestly that God should answer them at once. But God can only reveal His will to a heart that is humble and tender and empty. God can only reveal His will in perplexities and special difficulties to a heart that has learned to obey and honor Him loyally in little things and in daily life.

That brings me to the *third* thought—*Note the disposition to which the Spirit reveals God's will.*

What do we read here? There were a number of

men ministering to the Lord and fasting, and the
Holy Ghost came and spoke to them. Some people understand this passage very much as they would in
reference to a missionary committee of our day. We
see there is an open field, and we have had our
missions in other fields, and we are going to get on to
that field. We have virtually settled that, and we
pray about it. But the position was a very different
one in those former days. I doubt whether any of
them thought of Europe, for later on even Paul himself tried to go back into Asia, till the night vision
called him by the will of God. Look at those men. God
had done wonders. He had extended the Church to
Antioch, and He had given rich and large blessing.
Now, here were these men ministering to the Lord,
serving Him with prayer and fasting. What a deep
conviction they have—"It must all come direct from
Heaven. We are in fellowship with the risen Lord;
we must have a close union with Him, and somehow
He will let us know what He wants." And there they
were, empty, ignorant, helpless, glad and joyful, but
deeply humbled.

"O Lord," they seem to say, "we are Thy servants, and in fasting and prayer we wait upon Thee.
What is Thy will for us?"

Was it not the same with Peter? He was on the
housetop, fasting and praying, and little did he think
of the vision and the command to go to Caesarea. He
was ignorant of what his work might be.

It is in hearts entirely surrendered to the Lord
Jesus, in hearts separating themselves from the
world, and even from ordinary religious exercises,
and giving themselves up in intense prayer to look to

their Lord—it is in such hearts that the heavenly will of God will be made manifest.

You know that word *fasting* occurs a second time (in the third verse): "They fasted and prayed." When you pray, you love to go into your closet, according to the command of Jesus, and shut the door. You shut out business and company and pleasure and anything that can distract, and you want to be alone with God. But in one way even the material world follows you there. You must eat. These men wanted to shut themselves out from the influences of the material and the visible, and they fasted. What they ate was simply enough to supply the wants of nature, and in the intensity of their souls they thought to give expression to their letting go of everything on earth in their fasting before God. Oh, may God give us that intensity of desire, that separation from everything, because we want to wait upon God, that the Holy Ghost may reveal to us God's blessed will.

The *fourth* thought—What is now the will of God as the Holy Ghost reveals it? It is contained in one phrase: *Separation unto the Holy Ghost.* That is the keynote of the message from Heaven.

"Separate me Barnabas and Saul for the work whereunto I have called them. The work is mine, and I care for it, and I have chosen these men and called them, and I want you who represent the Church of Christ upon earth to set them apart unto me."

Look at this heavenly message in its twofold aspect. The men were to be *set apart* to the Holy Ghost, and *the Church was to do this separating work.* The Holy Ghost could trust these men to do it in a right spirit. There they were abiding in fellowship with the heavenly, and the Holy Ghost could say to them, "Do the work of separating these men." And these were the men the Holy Ghost had prepared, and He could say of them, "Let them be separated unto me."

Here we come to the very root, to the very life of the need of Christian workers. The question is: What is needed that the power of God should rest upon us more mightily, that the blessing of God should be poured out more abundantly among those poor, wretched people and perishing sinners among whom we labor? And the answer from Heaven is:

"I want men separated unto the Holy Ghost."

What does that imply? You know that there are two spirits on earth. Christ said, when He spoke about the Holy Spirit: "The world cannot receive him." Paul said: "We have received not the spirit of the world, but the Spirit that is of God." That is the great want in every worker—the spirit of the world going out, and the Spirit of God coming in to take possession of the inner life and of the whole being.

I am sure there are workers who often cry to God for the Holy Spirit to come upon them as a Spirit of power for their work, and when they feel that measure of power, and get blessing, they thank God for it. But God wants something more and something higher. God wants us to seek for the Holy Spirit as a Spirit of power in our own heart and life, to conquer self and cast out sin, and to work the blessed and beautiful image of Jesus into us.

There is a difference between the power of the Spirit as a gift, and the power of the Spirit for the

grace of a holy life. A man may often have a measure
of the power of the Spirit, but if there be not a large
measure of the Spirit as the Spirit of grace and
holiness, the defect will be manifest in his work. He
may be made the means of conversion, but he never
will help people on to a higher standard of spiritual
life, and when he passes away, a great deal of his
work may pass away too. But a man who is
separated unto the Holy Ghost is a man who is given
up to say:

"Father, let the Holy Ghost have full dominion
over me, in my home, in my temper, in every word of
my tongue, in every thought of my heart, in every
feeling toward my fellow men; let the Holy Spirit
have entire possession."

Is that what has been the longing and the
covenant of your heart with your God—to be a man
or a woman separated and given up unto the Holy
Ghost? I pray you listen to the voice of Heaven.
"Separate me," said the Holy Ghost. Yes, *separated*
unto the Holy Ghost. May God grant that the Word
may enter into the very depths of our being to search
us, and if we discover that we have not come out
from the world entirely, if God discovers to us that
the self-life, self-will, self-exaltation are there, let us
humble ourselves before Him.

Man, woman, brother, sister, you are a worker
separated unto the Holy Ghost. Is that true? Has that
been your longing desire? Has that been your
surrender? Has that been what you have expected
through faith in the power of our risen and almighty
Lord Jesus? If not, here is the call of faith, and here

is the key of blessing—*separated unto the Holy Ghost.* God write the word in our hearts!

I said the Holy Spirit spoke to that church as a church capable of doing that work. The Holy Spirit trusted them. God grant that our churches, our missionary societies, and our workers' unions, that all our directors and councils and committees may be men and women who are *fit for the work of separating workers unto the Holy Spirit.* We can ask God for that too.

Then comes my *fifth* thought, and it is this—*This holy partnership with the Holy Spirit in this work becomes a matter of consciousness and of action.*

These men, what did they do? They set apart Paul and Barnabas, and then it is written of the two that they, being sent forth by the Holy Ghost, went down to Seleucia. Oh, what fellowship! The Holy Spirit in Heaven doing part of the work, men on earth doing the other part. After the ordination of the men upon earth, it is written in God's inspired Word that they were sent forth by the Holy Ghost.

And see how this partnership calls to new prayer and fasting. They had for a certain time been ministering to the Lord and fasting, perhaps days; and the Holy Spirit speaks, and they have to do the work and to enter into partnership, and at once they come together for more prayer and fasting. That is the spirit in which they obey the command of their Lord. And that teaches us that it is not only in the beginning of our Christian work, but all along that we need to have our strength in prayer. If there is one thought with regard to the Church of Christ, which at times comes to me with overwhelming sorrow; if there is one thought in regard to my own life of which I am ashamed; if there is one thought of which I feel that the Church of Christ has not accepted it and not grasped it; if there is one thought which makes me pray to God: "Oh, teach us by Thy grace, new things"—it is the wonderful power that prayer is meant to have in the kingdom. We have so little availed ourselves of it.

We have all read the expression of Christian in Bunyan's great work, when he found he had the key in his breast that should unlock the dungeon. We have the key that can unlock the dungeon of atheism and of heathendom. But, oh! we are far more occupied with our work than we are with prayer. We believe more in speaking to men than we believe in speaking to God. Learn from these men that the work which the Holy Ghost commands must call us to new fasting and prayer, to new separation from the spirit and the pleasures of the world, to new consecration to God and to His fellowship. Those men gave themselves up to fasting and prayer, and if in all our ordinary Christian work there were more prayer, there would be more blessing in our own inner life. If we felt and proved and testified to the world that our only strength lay in keeping every minute in contact with Christ, every minute allowing God to work in us—if that were our spirit, would not, by the grace of God, our lives be holier? Would not they be more abundantly fruitful?

I hardly know a more solemn warning in God's Word than that which we find in the third chapter of Galatians, where Paul asked:

"Having begun in the Spirit, are ye now made perfect by the flesh?"

Do you understand what that means? A terrible danger in Christian work, just as in a Christian life that is begun with much prayer, begun in the Holy Spirit, is that it may be gradually shunted off on to the lines of the flesh; and the word comes: "Having begun in the Spirit, are ye now made perfect by the flesh?" In the time of our first perplexity and helplessness we prayed much to God, and God answered and God blessed, and our organization became perfected, and our band of workers became large; but gradually the organization and the work and the rush have so taken possession of us that the power of the Spirit, in which we began when we were a small company, has almost been lost. Oh, I pray you, note it well! It was with new prayer and fasting, with more prayer and fasting, that this company of disciples carried out the command of the Holy Ghost, "My soul, wait thou only upon God." That is our highest and most important work. The Holy Spirit comes in answer to believing prayer.

You know when the exalted Jesus had ascended to the throne, for ten days the footstool of the throne was the place where His waiting disciples cried to Him. And that is the law of the kingdom—the King upon the throne, the servants upon the footstool. May God find us there unceasingly!

Then comes the *last* thought—*What a wonderful blessing comes when the Holy Ghost is allowed to lead and to direct the work, and when it is carried on in obedience to Him!*

You know the story of the mission on which Bar-

nabas and Saul were sent out. You know what
power there was with them. The Holy Ghost sent
them, and they went on from place to place with
large blessing. The Holy Ghost was their leader further on. You recollect how it was by the Spirit that
Paul was hindered from going again into Asia, and
was led away over to Europe. Oh, the blessing that
rested upon that little company of men, and upon
their ministry unto the Lord!

I pray you, let us learn to believe that God has a
blessing for us. The Holy Ghost, into whose hands
God has put the work, has been called "the
executive of the Holy Trinity." The Holy Ghost has
not only power, but He has the Spirit of love. He is
brooding over this dark world and every sphere of
work in it, and He is willing to bless. And why is
there not more blessing? There can be but one answer. We have not honored the Holy Ghost as we
should have done. Is there one who can say that that
is not true? Is not every thoughtful heart ready to
cry: "God forgive me that I have not honored the
Holy Spirit as I should have done, that I have grieved
Him, that I have allowed self and the flesh and my
own will to work where the Holy Ghost should have
been honored! May God forgive me that I have
allowed self and the flesh and the will actually to
have the place that God wanted the Holy Ghost to
have."

Oh, the sin is greater than we know! No wonder
that there is so much feebleness and failure in the
Church of Christ!

PETER'S REPENTANCE

"And the Lord turned, and looked upon Peter. And Peter remembered the word of the Lord, how he had said unto him, Before the cock crow, thou shalt deny me thrice. And Peter went out, and wept bitterly" (LUKE 22: 61, 62).

THAT WAS THE TURNING-POINT in the history of Peter. Christ had said to him: "Thou canst not follow me now." Peter was not in a fit state to follow Christ, because he had not been brought to an end of himself; he did not know himself, and he therefore could not follow Christ. But when he went out and wept bitterly, then came the great change. Christ previously said to him: "When thou art converted, strengthen thy brethren." Here is the point where Peter was converted from self to Christ.

I thank God for the story of Peter. I do not know a man in the Bible who gives us greater comfort. When we look at his character, so full of failures, and at what Christ made him by the power of the Holy Ghost, there is hope for every one of us. But remember, before Christ could fill Peter with the Holy Spirit and make a new man of him, he had to go out and weep bitterly; he had to be humbled. If we want

to understand this, I think there are four points that
we must look at. First, let us look at *Peter the
devoted disciple of Jesus*; next, *at Peter as he lived
the life of self*; then at *Peter in his repentance*; and
last, at *what Christ made of Peter by the Holy Spirit.*

PETER THE DEVOTED DISCIPLE OF CHRIST

Christ called Peter to forsake his nets, and follow
Him. Peter did it at once, and he afterward could say
rightly to the Lord:

"We have forsaken all and followed thee."

Peter was a man of *absolute surrender;* he gave
up all to follow Jesus. Peter was also a man of
ready obedience. You remember Christ said to him,
"Launch out into the deep, and let down the net."
Peter the fisherman knew there were no fish there,
for they had been toiling all night and had caught
nothing; but he said: "At thy word I will let down the
net." He submitted to the word of Jesus. Further, he
was a man of *great faith.* When he saw Christ
walking on the sea, he said: "Lord, if it be thou, bid
me come unto thee"; and at the voice of Christ he
stepped out of the boat and walked upon the water.

And Peter was a man of *spiritual insight.* When
Christ asked the disciples: "Whom do ye say that I
am?" Peter was able to answer: "Thou art the
Christ, the Son of the livng God." And Christ said:
"Blessed art thou, Simon Barjona; for flesh and
blood hath not revealed it unto thee, but my Father
which is in heaven." And Christ spoke of him as the
rock man, and of his having the keys of the kingdom.
Peter was a splendid man, a devoted disciple of
Jesus, and if he were living nowadays, everyone

would say that he was an advanced Christian. And
yet how much there was wanting in Peter!

PETER LIVING THE LIFE OF SELF

You recollect that just after Christ had said to
him: "Flesh and blood hath not revealed it unto thee,
but my Father which is in heaven," Christ began to
speak about His sufferings, and Peter dared to say:
"Be it far from thee, Lord; this shall not be unto
thee." Then Christ had to say:

"Get thee behind me, Satan; for thou savorest not
the things that be of God, but those that be of men."

There was Peter in his self-will, trusting his own
wisdom, and actually forbidding Christ to go and die.
Whence did that come? Peter trusted in himself and
his own thoughts about divine things. We see later
on, more than once, that among the disciples there
was a questioning who should be the greatest, and
Peter was one of them, and he thought he had a right
to the very first place. He sought his own honor even
above the others. It was the life of self strong in
Peter. He had left his boats and his nets, but not his
old self.

When Christ had spoken to him about His sufferings, and said: "Get thee behind me, Satan," He
followed it up by saying: "If any man will come after
me, let him deny himself, and take up his cross, and
follow me." No man can follow Him unless he do
that. Self must be utterly denied. What does that
mean? When Peter denied Christ, we read that he
said three times: "I do not know the man"; in other
words: "I have nothing to do with Him; He and I are

no friends; I deny having any connection with Him."
Christ told Peter that he must deny self. Self must be
ignored, and its every claim rejected. That is the
root of true discipleship; but Peter did not understand it, and could not obey it. And what happened? When the last night came, Christ said to him:

"Before the cock crow twice thou shalt deny me
thrice."

But with what self-confidence Peter said: "Though
all should forsake thee, yet will not I. I am ready to
go with thee, to prison and to death."

Peter meant it honestly, and Peter really intended
to do it; but Peter did not know himself. He did not
believe he was as bad as Jesus said he was.

We perhaps think of individual sins that come between us and God, but what are we to do with that
self-life which is all unclean, our very nature? What
are we to do with that flesh that is entirely under the
power of sin? Deliverance from that is what we
need. Peter knew it not, and therefore it was that in
his self-confidence he went forth and denied his
Lord.

Notice how Christ uses that word *deny* twice. He
said to Peter the first time, *"Deny self"*; He said to
Peter the second time, *"Thou wilt deny me."* It is
either of the two. There is no choice for us; we must
either deny self or deny Christ. There are two great
powers fighting each other—the self-nature in the
power of sin, and Christ in the power of God. Either
of these must rule within us.

It was self that made the Devil. He was an angel of
God, but he wanted to exalt self. He became a Devil
in Hell. Self was the cause of the fall of man. Eve

wanted something for herself, and so our first
parents fell into all the wretchedness of sin. We
their children have inherited an awful nature of sin.

PETER'S REPENTANCE

Peter denied his Lord thrice, and then the Lord
looked upon him; and that look of Jesus broke the
heart of Peter, and all at once there opened up
before him the terrible sin that he had committed,
the terrible failure that had come, and the depth into
which he had fallen, and "Peter went out and wept
bitterly."

Oh! who can tell what that repentance must have
been? During the following hours of that night, and
the next day, when he saw Christ crucified and
buried, and the next day, the Sabbath—oh, in what
hopeless despair and shame he must have spent that
day!

"My Lord is gone, my hope is gone, and I denied
my Lord. After that life of love, after that blessed
fellowship of three years, I denied my Lord. God
have mercy upon me!"

I do not think we can realize into what a depth of
humiliation Peter sank then. But that was the
turningpoint and the change; and on the first day of
the week Christ was seen of Peter, and in the
evening He met him with the others. Later on at the
Lake of Galilee He asked him: "Lovest thou me?" until Peter was made sad by the thought that the Lord
reminded him of having denied Him thrice; and said
in sorrow, but in uprightness:

"Lord, thou knowest all things; thou knowest that
I love thee."

PETER TRANSFORMED

Now Peter was prepared for deliverance from
self, and that is my last thought. You know Christ
took him with others to the footstool of the throne,
and bade them wait there; and then on the day of
Pentecost the Holy Spirit came, and Peter was a
changed man. I do not want you to think only of the
change in Peter, in that boldness, and that power,
and that insight into the Scriptures, and that
blessing with which he preached that day. Thank
God for that. But there was something for Peter
deeper and better. Peter's whole nature was
changed. The work that Christ began in Peter when
He looked upon him, was perfected when he was
filled with the Holy Ghost.

If you want to see that, read the First Epistle of
Peter. You know wherein Peter's failings lay. When
he said to Christ, in effect: "Thou never canst suffer;
it cannot be"—it showed he had not a conception of
what it was to pass through death into life. Christ
said: "Deny *thyself*," and in spite of that he denied
his Lord. When Christ warned him: "Thou shalt
deny me," and he insisted that he never would, Peter
showed how little he understood what there was in
himself. But when I read his epistle and hear him
say: "If ye be reproached for the name of Christ,
happy are ye, for the Spirit of God and of glory
resteth upon you," then I say that it is not the old
Peter, but that is the very Spirit of Christ breathing
and speaking within him.

I read again how he says: "Hereunto ye are
called, to suffer, even as Christ suffered." I un-

derstand what a change had come over Peter. Instead of denying Christ, he found joy and pleasure in having self denied and crucified and given up to the death. And therefore it is in the Acts we read that, when he was called before the Council, he could boldly say: "We must obey God rather than men," and that he could return with the other disciples and rejoice that they were counted worthy to suffer for Christ's name.

You remember his self-exaltation; but now he has found out that "the ornament of a meek and quiet spirit is in the sight of God of great price." Again he tells us to be "subject one to another, and be clothed with humility."

Dear friend, I beseech you, look at Peter utterly changed—the self-pleasing, the self-trusting, the self-seeking Peter, full of sin, continually getting into trouble, foolish and impetuous, but now filled with the Spirit and the life of Jesus. Christ had done it for him by the Holy Ghost.

And now, what is my object in having thus very briefly pointed to the story of Peter? That story must be the history of every believer who is really to be made a blessing by God. That story is a prophecy of what everyone can receive from God in Heaven.

Now let us just glance hurriedly at what these lessons teach us.

The *first lesson* is this—You may be a very earnest, godly, devoted believer, in whom the power of the flesh is yet very strong.

That is a very solemn truth. Peter, before he denied Christ, had cast out devils and had healed the sick; and yet the flesh had power, and the flesh had

room in him. Oh, beloved, we want to realize that it
is just because there is so much of that self-
life in us that the power of God cannot work in us as
mightily as God is willing that it should work. Do you
realize that the great God is longing to double His
blessing, to give tenfold blessing through us? But
there is something hindering Him, and that
something is a proof of nothing but the self-life. We
talk about the pride of Peter, and the impetuosity of
Peter, and the self-confidence of Peter. It all rooted
in that one word, *self.* Christ had said, "Deny self,"
and Peter had never understood, and never obeyed;
and every failing came out of that.

What a solemn thought, and what an urgent plea
for us to cry: O God, do discover this to us, that none
of us may be living the self-life! It has happened to
many a one who had been a Christian for years, who
had perhaps occupied a prominent position, that
God found him out and taught him to find himself out,
and he became utterly ashamed, falling down
broken before God. Oh, the bitter shame and sorrow
and pain and agony that came to him, until at last he
found that there was deliverance! Peter went out
and wept bitterly, and there may be many a godly
one in whom the power of the flesh still rules.

And then my *second lesson* is—It is the work of
our blessed Lord Jesus to discover the power of self.

How was it that Peter, the carnal Peter, self-
willed Peter, Peter with the strong self-love, ever
became a man of Pentecost and the writer of his
epistle? It was because Christ had him in charge,
and Christ watched over him, and Christ taught and
blessed him. The warnings that Christ had given him

were part of the training; and last of all there came
that look of love. In His suffering Christ did not
forget him, but turned round and looked upon him,
and "Peter went out and wept bitterly." And the
Christ who led Peter to Pentecost is waiting today to
take charge of every heart that is willing to surrender itself to Him.

Are there not some saying: "Ah! that is the
mischief with me; it is always the self-life, and self-
comfort, and self-consciousness, and self-pleasing,
and self-will; how am I to get rid of it?"

My answer is: It is Christ Jesus who can rid you of
it; none else but Christ Jesus can give deliverance
from the power of self. And what does He ask you to
do? He asks that you should humble yourself before
Him.

IMPOSSIBLE WITH MAN, POSSIBLE WITH GOD

"*And he said, The things which are impossible with men are possible with God*" (LUKE 18:27).

CHRIST HAD SAID to the rich young ruler, "Sell all that thou hast . . . and come, follow me." The young man went away sorrowful. Christ then turned to the disciples, and said: "How hardly shall they that have riches enter into the kingdom of God!" The disciples, we read, were greatly astonished, and answered: "If it is so difficult to enter the kingdom, who, then, can be saved?" And Christ gave this blessed answer:

"The things which are impossible with men are possible with God."

The text contains two thoughts—that *in religion, in the question of salvation and of following Christ by a holy life, it is impossible for man to do it.* And then alongside that is the thought—*What is impossible with man is possible with God.*

The two thoughts mark the two great lessons that man has to learn in the religious life. It often takes a long time to learn the first lesson, that in religion man can do nothing, that salvation is impossible to man. And often a man learns that, and yet he does not learn the second lesson—what has been impossible to him is possible with God. Blessed is the man who learns both lessons! The learning of them marks stages in the Christian's life.

Man Cannot

The one stage is when a man is trying to do his utmost and fails, when a man tries to do better and fails again, when a man tries much more and always fails. And yet very often he does not even then learn the lesson: *With man it is impossible to serve God and Christ.* Peter spent three years in Christ's school, and he never learned that, *It is impossible,* until he had denied his Lord and went out and wept bitterly. Then he learned it.

Just look for a moment at a man who is learning this lesson. At first he fights against it; then he submits to it, but reluctantly and in despair; at last he accepts it willingly and rejoices in it. At the beginning of the Christian life the young convert has no conception of this truth. He has been converted, he has the joy of the Lord in his heart, he begins to run the race and fight the battle; he is sure he can conquer, for he is earnest and honest, and God will help him. Yet, somehow, very soon he fails where he did not expect it, and sin gets the better of him. He is disappointed; but he thinks: "I was not watchful enough, I did not make my resolutions strong enough." And again he vows, and again he prays, and yet he fails. He thought: "Am I not a regenerate man? Have I not the life of God within me?" And he thinks again: "Yes, and I have Christ to help me, I can live the holy life."

At a later period he comes to another state of mind. He begins to see such a life is impossible, but he does not accept it. There are multitudes of Christians who come to this point: "I cannot"; and then think God never expected them to do what they cannot do. If you tell them that God does expect it, it appears to them a mystery. A good many Christians are living a low life, a life of failure and of sin, instead of rest and victory, because they began to see: "I cannot, it is impossible." And yet they do not understand it fully, and so, under the impression, *I cannot*, they give way to despair. They will do their best, but they never expect to get on very far.

But God leads His children on to a third stage, when a man comes to take that, *It is impossible,* in its full truth, and yet at the same time says: "I must do it, and I will do it—it is impossible for man, and yet I must do it"; when the renewed will begins to exercise its whole power, and in intense longing and prayer begins to cry to God: "Lord, what is the meaning of this?—how am I to be freed from the power of sin?"

It is the state of the regenerate man in Romans 7. There you will find the Christian man trying his very utmost to live a holy life. God's law has been revealed to him as reaching down into the very depth of the desires of the heart, and the man can dare to say:

"I delight in the law of God after the inward man. To will what is good is present with me. My heart loves the law of God, and my will has chosen that law."

Can a man like that fail, with his heart full of delight in God's law and with his will determined to do what is right? Yes. That is what Romans 7 teaches us. There is something more needed. Not only must I delight in the law of God after the inward man, and will what God wills, but I need a divine omnipotence to work it in me. And that is what the apostle Paul teaches in Philippians 2:13:

"It is God which worketh in you, both to will and to do."

Note the contrast. In Romans 7, the regenerate man says: "To will is present with me, but to do—I find I cannot do. I will, but I cannot perform." But in Philippians 2, you have a man who has been led on farther, a man who understands that when God has worked the renewed will, God will give the power to accomplish what that will desires. Let us receive this as the first great lesson in the spiritual life:"It is impossible for me, my God; let there be an end of the flesh and all its powers, an end of self, and let it be my glory to be helpless."

Praise God for the divine teaching that makes us helpless!

When you thought of absolute surrender to God were you not brought to an end of yourself, and to feel that you could see how you actually could live as a man absolutely surrendered to God every moment of the day—at your table, in your house, in your business, in the midst of trials and temptations? I pray you learn the lesson now. If you felt you could not do it, you are on the right road, if you let your-

selves be led. Accept that position, and maintain it
before God: "My heart's desire and delight, O God,
is absolute surrender, but I cannot perform it. It is
impossible for me to live that life. It is beyond me."
Fall down and learn that when you are utterly
helpless, God will come to work in you not only to
will, but also to do.

God Can

Now comes the second lesson. "The things which
are impossible with men *are possible with God.*"

I said a little while ago that there is many a man
who has learned the lesson, *It is impossible with
men,* and then he gives up in helpless despair, and
lives a wretched Christian life, without joy, or
strength, or victory. And why? Because he does not
humble himself to learn that other lesson: *With God
all things are possible.*

Your religious life is every day to be a proof that
God works impossibilities; your religious life is to be
a series of impossibilities made possible and actual
by God's almighty power. That is what the Christian
needs. He has an almighty God that he worships, and
he must learn to understand that he does not need a
little of God's power, but he needs—with reverence
be it said—the whole of God's omnipotence to keep
him right, and to live like a Christian.

The whole of Christianity is a work of God's omnipotence. Look at the birth of Christ Jesus. That was
a miracle of divine power, and it was said to Mary:
"With God nothing shall be impossible." It was the
omnipotence of God. Look at Christ's resurrection.

We are taught that it was according to the exceeding greatness of His mighty power that God raised Christ from the dead.

Every tree must grow on the root from which it springs. An oak tree three hundred years old grows all the time on the one root from which it had its beginning. Christianity had its beginning in the omnipotence of God, and in every soul it must have its continuance in that omnipotence. All the possibilities of the higher Christian life have their origin in a new apprehension of Christ's power to work all God's will in us.

I want to call upon you now to come and worship an almighty God. Have you learned to do it? Have you learned to deal so closely with an almighty God that you know omnipotence is working in you? In outward appearance there is often so little sign of it. The apostle Paul said: "I was with you in weakness and in fear and in much trembling, and . . . my preaching was . . . in demonstration of the Spirit and of power." From the human side there was feebleness, from the divine side there was divine omnipotence. And that is true of every godly life; and if we would only learn that lesson better, and give a wholehearted, undivided surrender to it, we should learn what blessedness there is in dwelling every hour and every moment with an almighty God. Have you ever studied in the Bible the attribute of God's omnipotence? You know that it was God's omnipotence that created the world, and created light out of darkness, and created man. But have you studied God's omnipotence in the works of redemption?

Look at Abraham. When God called him to be the
father of that people out of which Christ was to be
born, God said to him: "I am God Almighty, walk
before me and be thou perfect." And God trained
Abraham to trust Him as the omnipotent One; and
whether it was his going out to a land that he knew
not, or his faith as a pilgrim midst the thousands of
Canaanites—his faith said: This is my land—or
whether it was his faith in waiting twenty-five years
for a son in his old age, against all hope, or whether
it was the raising up of Isaac from the dead on
Mount Moriah when he was going to sacrifice
him—Abraham believed God. He was strong in faith,
giving glory to God, because he accounted Him who
had promised able to perform.

The cause of the weakness of your Christian life is
that you want to work it out partly, and to let God
help you. And that cannot be. You must come to be
utterly helpless, to let God work, and God will work
gloriously. It is this that we need if we are indeed to
be workers for God. I could go through Scripture and
prove to you how Moses, when he led Israel out of
Egypt; how Joshua, when he brought them into the
land of Canaan; how all God's servants in the Old
Testament counted upon the omnipotence of God
doing impossibilities. And this God lives today, and
this God is the God of every child of His. And yet we
are some of us wanting God to give us a little help
while we do our best, instead of coming to understand what God wants, and to say: "I can do
nothing. God must and will do all." Have you said:
"In worship, in work, in sanctification, in obedience
to God, I can do nothing of myself, and so my place is

to worship the omnipotent God, and to believe that He will work in me every moment"? Oh, may God teach us this! Oh, that God would by His grace show you what a God you have, and to what a God you have entrusted yourself—an omnipotent God, willing with His whole omnipotence to place Himself at the disposal of every child of His! Shall we not take the lesson of the Lord Jesus and say: "Amen; the things which are impossible with men are possible with God"?

Remember what we have said about Peter, his self-confidence, self-power, self-will, and how he came to deny his Lord. You feel, "Ah! there is the self-life, there is the flesh-life that rules in me!" And now, have you believed that there is deliverance from that? Have you believed that Almighty God is able so to reveal Christ in your heart, so to let the Holy Spirit rule in you, that the self-life shall not have power or dominion over you? Have you coupled the two together, and with tears of penitence and with deep humiliation and feebleness, cried out: "O God, it is impossible to me; man cannot do it, but, glory to Thy name, it is possible with God"? Have you claimed deliverance? Do it now. Put yourself afresh in absolute surrender into the hands of a God of infinite love; and as infinite as His love is His power to do it.

GOD WORKS IN MAN

But again, we came to the question of absolute surrender, and felt that that is the want in the Church of Christ, and that is why the Holy Ghost cannot fill us, and why we cannot live as people entirely separated unto the Holy Ghost; that is why the flesh and the self-life cannot be conquered. We have never understood what it is to be absolutely surrendered to God as Jesus was. I know that many a one earnestly and honestly says: "Amen, I accept the message of absolute surrender to God"; and yet thinks: "Will that ever be mine? Can I count upon God to make me one of whom it shall be said in Heaven and on earth and in Hell, he lives in absolute surrender to God?" Brother, sister, "the things which are impossible with men are possible with God." Do believe that when He takes charge of you in Christ, it is possible for God to make you a man of absolute surrender. And God is able to maintain that. He is able to let you rise from bed every morning of the week with that blessed thought directly or indirectly: "I am in God's charge. My God is working out my life for me."

Some are weary of thinking about sanctification. You pray, you have longed and cried for it, and yet it appeared so far off! The holiness and humility of Jesus—you are so conscious of how distant it is. Beloved friends, the one doctrine of sanctification that is scriptural and real and effectual is: "The things which are impossible with men are possible with God." God can sanctify men, and by His almighty and sanctifying power every moment God can keep them. Oh, that we might get a step nearer to our God now! Oh, that the light of God might shine, and that we might know our God better!

I could go on to speak about the life of Christ in us—living like Christ, taking Christ as our Saviour from sin, and as our life and strength. It is God in Heaven who can reveal that in you. What does that prayer of the apostle Paul say: "That he would grant you according to riches of his glory"—it is sure to be something very wonderful if it is according to the riches of His glory—"to be strengthened with might by his Spirit in the inner man"? Do you not see that it is an omnipotent God working by His omnipotence in the heart of His believing children, so that Christ can become an indwelling Saviour? You have tried to grasp it and to seize it, and you have tried to believe it, and it would not come. It was because you had not been brought to believe that "the things which are impossible with men are possible with God."

And so, I trust that the word spoken about love may have brought many to see that we must have an inflowing of love in quite a new way; our heart must be filled with life from above, from the Fountain of everlasting love, if it is going to overflow all the day; then it will be just as natural for us to love our fellowmen as it is natural for the lamb to be gentle and the wolf to be cruel. Until I am brought to such a state that the more a man hates and speaks evil of me, the more unlikable and unlovable a man is, I shall love him all the more; until I am brought to such a state that the more the obstacles and hatred and ingratitude, the more can the power of love triumph in me—until I am brought to see that, I am not saying: "It is impossible with men." But if you have been led to say: "This message has spoken to me about a love utterly beyond my power; it is absolutely impossible"—then we can come to God and say: "It is possible with Thee."

Some are crying to God for a great revival. I can say that that is the prayer of my heart unceasingly. Oh, if God would only revive His believing people! I cannot think in the first place of the unconverted formalists of the Church, or of the infidels and skeptics, or of all the wretched and perishing around me, my heart prays in the first place: "My God, revive Thy Church and people." It is not for nothing that there are in thousands of hearts yearnings after holiness and consecration: it is a forerunner of God's power. God works *to will* and then He works *to do*. These yearnings are a witness and a proof that God has worked *to will*. Oh, let us in faith believe that the omnipotent God will work *to do* among His people more than we can ask. "Unto him," Paul said, "who is able to do exceeding abundantly above all that we ask or think, . . . unto him be glory." Let our hearts say that. Glory to God, the omnipotent One, who can do above what we dare to ask or think!

"The things which are impossible with men are possible with God." All around you there is a world of sin and sorrow, and the Devil is there. But remember, Christ is on the throne, Christ is stronger, Christ has conquered, and Christ will conquer. But wait on God. My text casts us down: "The things which are *impossible with men*"; but it ultimately lifts us up high—"are *possible with God*." Get linked to God. Adore and trust Him as the omnipotent One, not only for your own life, but for all the souls that are entrusted to you. Never pray without adoring His omnipotence, saying: "*Mighty God, I claim Thine almightiness.*" And the answer to the prayer will come, and like Abraham you will become strong in faith, giving glory to God, because you account Him who hath promised able to perform.

"O WRETCHED MAN THAT I AM!"

"O wretched man that I am! who shall deliver me from the body of this death? I thank God through Jesus Christ our Lord" (ROMANS 7:24, 25).

YOU KNOW the wonderful place that this text has in the wonderful epistle to the Romans. It stands here at the end of the seventh chapter as the gateway into the eighth. In the first sixteen verses of the eighth chapter the name of the Holy Spirit is found sixteen times; you have there the description and promise of the life that a child of God can live in the power of the Holy Ghost. This begins in the second verse: "The law of the Spirit of life in Christ Jesus hath made me free from the law of sin and death." From that Paul goes on to speak of the great privileges of the child of God, who is to be led by the Spirit of God. The gateway into all this is in the twenty-fourth verse of the seventh chapter:

"O wretched man that I am!"

There you have the words of a man who has come to the end of himself. He has in the previous verses described how he had struggled and wrestled in his own power to obey the holy law of God, and had

70

failed. But in answer to his own question he now finds the true answer and cries out: "I thank God through Jesus Christ our Lord." From that he goes on to speak of what that deliverance is that he has found.

I want from these words to describe the path by which a man can be led out of the spirit of bondage into the spirit of liberty. You know how distinctly it is said: "Ye have not received the spirit of bondage again to fear." We are continually warned that this is the great danger of the Christian life, to go again into bondage; and I want to describe the path by which a man can get out of bondage into the glorious liberty of the children of God. Rather, I want to describe the man himself.

First, these words are the language of a *regenerate* man; *second,* of an *impotent* man; *third,* of a *wretched* man; and *fourth,* of a man *on the borders of complete liberty.*

THE REGENERATE MAN

There is much evidence of regeneration from the fourteenth verse of the chapter on to the twenty-third. "It is no more I that do it, but sin that dwelleth in me": that is the language of a regenerate man, a man who knows that his heart and nature have been renewed, and that sin is now a power in him that is not himself. "I delight in the law of the Lord after the inward man": that again is the language of a regenerate man. He dares to say when he does evil: "It is no more I that do it, but sin that dwelleth in me." It is of great importance to understand this.

In the first two great sections of the epistle, Paul

deals with justification and sanctification. In dealing with justification, he lays the foundation of the doctrine in the teaching about sin, not in the singular *sin*, but in the plural, *sins*—the actual transgressions. In the second part of the fifth chapter he begins to deal with sin, not as actual transgression, but as a power. Just imagine what a loss it would have been to us if we had not this second half of the seventh chapter of the Epistle to the Romans, if Paul had omitted in his teaching this vital question of the sinfulness of the believer. We should have missed the question we all want answered as to sin in the believer. What is the answer? The regenerate man is one in whom the will has been renewed, and who can say: "I delight in the law of God after the inward man."

The Impotent Man

Here is the great mistake made by many Christian people: they think that when there is a renewed will, it is enough; but that is not the case. This regenerate man tells us: "*I will* to do what is good, but *the power to perform* I find not." How often people tell us that if you set yourself determinedly, you can perform what you will! But this man was as determined as any man can be, and yet he made the confession: "To will is present with me; but how to perform that which is good, I find not."

But, you ask: "How is it God makes a regenerate man utter such a confession, with a right will, with a heart that longs to do good, and longs to do its very utmost to love God?"

Let us look at this question. What has God given us our will for? Had the angels who fell, in their own will, the strength to stand? Verily, no. The will of the creature is nothing but an empty vessel in which the power of God is to be made manifest. The creature must seek in God all that it is to be. You have it in the second chapter of the epistle to the Philippians, and you have it here also, that God's work is to work in us both to *will* and to *do* of His good pleasure. Here is a man who appears to say: "God has not worked to *do* in me." But we are taught that God works both to will and to do. How is the apparent contradiction to be reconciled?

You will find that in this passage (Rom. 7:6-25) the name of the Holy Spirit does not occur once, nor does the name of Christ occur. The man is wrestling and struggling to fulfill God's law. Instead of the Holy Spirit and of Christ, the law is mentioned nearly twenty times. In this chapter, it shows a believer doing his very best to obey the law of God with his regenerate will. Not only this; but you will find the little words, *I, me, my,* occur more than forty times. It is the regenerate *I* in its impotence seeking to obey the law without being filled with the Spirit. This is the experience of almost every saint. After conversion a man begins to do his best, and he fails; but if we are brought into the full light, we need fail no longer. Nor need we fail at all if we have received the Spirit in His fullness at conversion.

God allows that failure that the regenerate man should be taught his own utter impotence. It is in the course of this struggle that there comes to us this sense of our utter sinfulness. It is God's way of

dealing with us. He allows that man to strive to fulfill
the law that, as he strives and wrestles, he may be
brought to this: "I am a regenerate child of God, but
I am utterly helpless to obey His law." See what
strong words are used all through the chapter to
describe this condition: "I am carnal, sold under
sin"; "I see another law in my members bringing me
into captivity"; and last of all, "O wretched man
that I am! who shall deliver me from the body of this
death?" This believer who bows here in deep con-
trition is utterly unable to obey the law of God.

The Wretched Man

*Not only is the man who makes this confession a
regenerate and an impotent man, but he is also a
wretched man.* He is utterly unhappy and miserable;
and what is it that makes him so utterly miserable?
It is because God has given him a nature that loves
Himself. He is deeply wretched because he feels he
is not obeying his God. He says, with brokenness of
heart: "It is not I that do it, but I am under the awful
power of sin, which is holding me down. It is I, and
yet not I: alas! alas! it is myself; so closely am I
bound up with it, and so closely is it intertwined with
my very nature." Blessed be God when a man learns
to say: "O wretched man that I am!" from the depth
of his heart. He is on the way to the eighth chapter of
Romans.

There are many who make this confession a pillow
for sin. They say that Paul had to confess his
weakness and helplessness in this way, what are
they that they should try to do better? So the call to

holiness is quietly set aside. Would God that every one of us had learned to say these words in the very spirit in which they are written here! When we hear sin spoken of as the abominable thing that God hates, do not many of us wince before the word? Would that all Christians who go on sinning and sinning would take this verse to heart. If ever you utter a sharp word say: "O wretched man that I am!" And every time you lose your temper, kneel down and understand that it never was meant by God that this was to be the state in which His child should remain. Would God that we would take this word into our daily life, and say it every time we are touched about our own honor, and every time we say sharp things, and every time we sin against the Lord God, and against the Lord Jesus Christ in His humility, and in His obedience, and in His self-sacrifice! Would to God you could forget everything else, and cry out: "O wretched man that I am! who shall deliver me from the body of this death?"

Why should you say this whenever you commit sin? Because it is when a man is brought to this confession that deliverance is at hand.

And remember it was not only the sense of being impotent and taken captive that made him wretched, but it was above all the sense of sinning against his God. The law was doing its work, making sin *exceeding sinful* in his sight. The thought of continually grieving God became utterly unbearable—it was this brought forth the piercing cry: "O wretched man!" As long as we talk and reason about our impotence and our failure, and only try to find out what Romans 7 means, it will profit us but little; but

when once every sin gives new intensity to the sense
of wretchedness, and we feel our whole state as one
of not only helplessness, but actual exceeding sinfulness, we shall be pressed not only to ask: "Who
shall deliver us?" but to cry: "I thank God through
Jesus Christ my Lord."

The Almost-Delivered Man

The man has tried to obey the beautiful law of
God. He has loved it, he has wept over his sin, he has
tried to conquer, he has tried to overcome fault after
fault, but every time he has ended in failure.

What did he mean by "the body of this death"?
Did he mean, my body when I die? Verily no. In the
eighth chapter you have the answer to this question
in the words: "If ye through the Spirit do mortify the
deeds of the body, ye shall live." That is the body of
death from which he is seeking deliverance.

And now he is on the brink of deliverance! In the
twenty-third verse of the seventh chapter we have
the words: "I see another law in my members,
warring against the law of my mind, and bringing me
into *captivity* to the law of sin which is in my members." It is *a captive* that cries: "O wretched man
that I am! who shall deliver me from the body of this
death?" He is a man who feels himself bound. But
look to the contrast in the second verse of the eighth
chapter: "The law of the Spirit of life in Christ Jesus
hath *made me free* from the law of sin and death."
That is the deliverance through Jesus Christ our
Lord; the *liberty* to the captive which the Spirit

brings. Can you keep captive any longer a man made free by the "law of the Spirit of life in Christ Jesus"?

But you say, the regenerate man, had not he the Spirit of Jesus when he spoke in the sixth chapter? Yes, *but he did not know what the Holy Spirit could do for him.*

God does not work by His Spirit as He works by a blind force in nature. He leads His people on as reasonable, intelligent beings, and therefore when He wants to give us that Holy Spirit whom He has promised, He brings us first to the end of self, to the conviction that though we have been striving to obey the law, we have failed. When we have come to the end of that, then He shows us that in the Holy Spirit we have the power of obedience, the power of victory, and the power of real holiness.

God works *to will,* and He is ready to work *to do,* but, alas! many Christians misunderstand this. They think because they have the will, it is enough, and that now they are able to do. This is not so. The new will is a permanent gift, an attribute of the new nature. The power to do is not a permanent gift, but must be each moment received from the Holy Spirit. It is the man who is conscious *of his own impotence as a believer* who will learn that by the Holy Spirit *he can live a holy life.* This man is on the brink of that great deliverance; the way has been prepared for the glorious eighth chapter. I now ask this solemn question: Where are you living? Is it with you, "O wretched man that I am! who shall deliver me?" with now and then a little experience of the power of the Holy Spirit? or is it, "I thank God through Jesus

Christ! The law of the Spirit hath set me free from
the law of sin and of death"?

What the Holy Spirit does is to give the victory. "If
ye through the Spirit do mortify the deeds of the
flesh, ye shall live." It is the Holy Ghost who does
this—the third Person of the Godhead. He it is who,
when the heart is opened wide to receive Him, comes
in and reigns there, and mortifies the deeds of the
body, day by day, hour by hour, and moment by
moment.

I want to bring this to a point. Remember, dear
friend, what we need is to come to decision and action. There are in Scripture two very different sorts
of Christians. The Bible speaks in *Romans, Corinthians* and *Galatians* about yielding to the flesh; and
that is the life of tens of thousands of believers. All
their lack of joy in the Holy Ghost, and their lack of
the liberty He gives, is just owing to the flesh. The
Spirit is within them, but the flesh rules the life. To
be led by the Spirit of God is what they need. Would
God that I could make every child of His realize what
it means that the everlasting God has given His dear
Son, Christ Jesus, to watch over you every day, and
that what you have to do is to trust; and that the
work of the Holy Spirit is to enable you every
moment to remember Jesus, and to trust Him! The
Spirit has come to keep the link with Him unbroken
every moment. Praise God for the Holy Ghost! We
are so accustomed to think of the Holy Spirit as a
luxury, for special times, or for special ministers
and men. But the Holy Spirit is necessary for every
believer, every moment of the day. Praise God you
have Him, and that He gives you the full experience

of the deliverance in Christ, as He makes you free from the power of sin.

Who longs to have the power and the liberty of the Holy Spirit? Oh, brother, bow before God in one final cry of despair:

"O God, must I go on sinning this way forever? Who shall deliver me, O wretched man that I am! from the body of this death?"

Are you ready to sink before God in that cry and seek the power of Jesus to dwell and work in you? Are you ready to say: "I thank God through Jesus Christ"?

What good does it do that we go to church or attend conventions, that we study our Bibles and pray, unless our lives are filled with the Holy Spirit? That is what God wants; and nothing else will enable us to live a life of power and peace. You know that when a minister or parent is using the catechism, when a question is asked an answer is expected. Alas! how many Christians are content with the question put here: "O wretched man that I am! who shall deliver me from the body of this death?" but never give the answer. Instead of answering, they are silent. Instead of saying: "I thank God through Jesus Christ our Lord," they are forever repeating the question without the answer. If you want the path to the full deliverance of Christ, and the liberty of the Spirit, the glorious liberty of the children of God, take it through the seventh chapter of Romans; and then say: "I thank God through Jesus Christ our Lord." Be not content to remain ever groaning, but say: "I, a wretched man, thank God, through Jesus Christ.

Even though I do not see it all, I am going to praise God."

There is deliverance, there is the liberty of the Holy Spirit. The kingdom of God *is* "joy in the Holy Ghost."

"HAVING BEGUN IN THE SPIRIT"

THE WORDS from which I wish to address you, you will find in the epistle to the Galatians, the third chapter, the third verse; let us read the second verse also: "This only would I learn of you, Received ye the Spirit by the works of the law, or by the hearing of faith? Are ye so foolish?" And then comes my text—"Having begun in the Spirit, are ye now made perfect by the flesh?"

When we speak of the quickening or the deepening or the strengthening of the spiritual life, we are thinking of something that is feeble and wrong and sinful; and it is a great thing to take our place before God with the confession:

"Oh, God, our spiritual life is not what it should be!"

May God work that in your heart, reader.

As we look round about on the church we see so many indications of feebleness and of failure, and of sin, and of shortcoming, that we are compelled to ask: Why is it? Is there any necessity for the church of Christ to be living in such a low state? Or is it actually possible that God's people should be living always in the joy and strength of their God?

Every believing heart must answer: It is possible.

Then comes the great question: Why is it, how is it to be accounted for, that God's church as a whole is so feeble, and that the great majority of Christians are not living up to their privileges? There must be a reason for it. Has God not given Christ His Almighty Son to be the Keeper of every believer, to make Christ an ever-present reality, and to impart and communicate to us all that we have in Christ? God has given His Son, and God has given His Spirit. How is it that believers do not live up to their privileges?

We find in more than one of the epistles a very solemn answer to that question. There are epistles, such as the first to the Thessalonians, where Paul writes to the Christians, in effect: "I want you to grow, to abound, to increase more and more." They were young, and there were things lacking in their faith, but their state was so far satisfactory, and gave him great joy, and he writes time after time: "I pray God that you may abound more and more; I write to you to increase more and more." But there are other epistles where he takes a very different tone, especially the epistles to the Corinthians and to the Galatians, and he tells them in many different ways what the one reason was, that they were not living as Christians ought to live; many were under the power of the flesh. My text is one example. He reminds them that by the preaching of faith they had received the Holy Spirit. He had preached Christ to them; they had accepted that Christ, and had received the Holy Spirit in power. But what happened? Having begun in the Spirit, they tried to perfect the work that the Spirit had begun in the flesh by their own effort. We find the same teaching in the epistle to the Corinthians.

Now, we have here a solemn discovery of what the great want is in the church of Christ. God has called the church of Christ to live in the power of the Holy Spirit, and the church is living for the most part in the power of human flesh, and of will and energy and effort apart from the Spirit of God. I doubt not that that is the case with many individual believers; and oh, if God will use me to give you a message from Him, my one message will be this: "If the church will return to acknowledge that the Holy Spirit is her strength and her help, and if the church will return to give up everything, and wait upon God to be filled with the Spirit, her days of beauty and gladness will return, and we shall see the glory of God revealed among us." This is my message to every individual believer: "Nothing will help you unless you come to understand that you must live every day under the power of the Holy Ghost."

God wants you to be a living vessel in whom the power of the Spirit is to be manifested every hour and every moment of your life, and God will enable you to be that.

Now let us try to learn that this word to the Galatians teaches us—some very simple thoughts. It shows us how (1) *the beginning of the Christian life is receiving the Holy Spirit.* It shows us (2) what great danger there is of forgetting that we are to live by the Spirit, and not live after the flesh. It shows us (3) *what are the fruits and the proofs of our seeking perfection in the flesh.* And then it suggests to us (4) *the way of deliverance from this state.*

RECEIVING THE HOLY SPIRIT

First of all, Paul says: *"Having begun in the Spirit."* Remember, the apostle not only preached justification by faith, but he preached something more. He preached this—the epistle is full of it—that justified men cannot live but by the Holy Spirit, and that therefore God gives to every justified man the Holy Spirit to seal him. The apostle says to them in effect more than once:

"How did you receive the Holy Spirit? Was it by the preaching of the law, or by the preaching of faith?"

He could point back to that time when there had been a mighty revival under his teaching. The power of God had been manifested, and the Galatians were compelled to confess:

"Yes, we have got the Holy Ghost: accepting Christ by faith, by faith we received the Holy Spirit."

Now, it is to be feared that there are many Christians who hardly know that when they believed, they received the Holy Ghost. A great many Christians can say: "I received pardon and I received peace." But if you were to ask them: "Have you received the Holy Ghost?" they would hesitate, and many, if they were to say Yes, would say it with hesitation; and they would tell you that they hardly knew what it was, since that time, to walk in the power of the Holy Spirit. Let us try and take hold of this great truth: The beginning of the true Christian life is to receive the Holy Ghost. And the work of every Christian minister is that which was the work of Paul—to remind his people that they received the

Holy Ghost, and must live according to His guidance and in His power.

If those Galatians who received the Holy Spirit in power were tempted to go astray by that terrible danger of perfecting in the flesh what had been begun in the Spirit, how much more danger do those Christians run who hardly ever know that they have received the Holy Spirit, or who, if they know it as a matter of belief, hardly ever think of it and hardly ever praise God for it!

NEGLECTING THE HOLY SPIRIT

But now look, in the second place, at *the great danger.*

You all know what shunting is on a railway. A locomotive with its train may be run in a certain direction, and the points at some place may not be properly opened or closed, and unobservingly it is shunted off to the right or to the left. And if that takes place, for instance, on a dark night, the train goes in the wrong direction, and the people might never know it until they have gone some distance.

And just so God gives Christians the Holy Spirit with this intention, that every day all their life should be lived in the power of the Spirit. A man cannot live one hour a godly life unless by the power of the Holy Ghost. He may live a proper, consistent life, as people call it, an irreproachable life, a life of virtue and diligent service; but to live a life acceptable to God, in the enjoyment of God's salvation and God's love, to live and walk in the power of the new

life—he cannot do it unless he be guided by the Holy
Spirit every day and every hour.

But now listen to the danger. The Galatians
received the Holy Ghost, but what was begun by the
Spirit they tried to perfect in the flesh. How? They
fell back again under Judaizing teachers who told
them they must be circumcised. They began to seek
their religion in external observances. And so Paul
uses that expression about those teachers who had
them circumcised, that "they sought to glory in their
flesh."

You sometimes hear the expression used, *religious
flesh*. What is meant by that? It is simply an expression made to give utterance to this thought: My
human nature and my human will and my human effort can be very active in religion, and after being
converted, and after receiving the Holy Ghost, I may
begin in my own strength to try to serve God.

I may be very diligent and doing a great deal, and
yet all the time it is more the work of human flesh
than of God's Spirit. What a solemn thought, that
man can, without noticing it, be shunted off from the
line of the Holy Ghost on to the line of the flesh; that
he can be most diligent and make great sacrifices,
and yet it is all in the power of the human will! Ah,
the great question for us to ask of God in self-
examination is that we may be shown whether our
religious life is lived more in the power of the flesh
than in the power of the Holy Spirit. A man may be a
preacher, he may work most diligently in his
ministry, a man may be a Christian worker, and
others may tell of him that he makes great sacrifices,
and yet you can feel there is a want about it. You feel

that he is not a spiritual man; there is no spirituality about his life. How many Christians there are about whom no one would ever think of saying: "What a spiritual man he is!" Ah! there is the weakness of the Church of Christ. It is all in that one word—*flesh*.

Now, the flesh may manifest itself in many ways. It may be manifested in fleshly wisdom. My mind may be most active about religion. I may preach or write or think or meditate, and delight in being occupied with things in God's Book and in God's Kingdom; and yet the power of the Holy Ghost may be markedly absent. I fear that if you take the preaching throughout the Church of Christ and ask why there is, alas! so little converting power in the preaching of the Word, why there is so much work and often so little result for eternity, why the Word has so little power to build up believers in holiness and in consecration—the answer will come: It is the absence of the power of the Holy Ghost. And why is this? There can be no other reason but that the flesh and human energy have taken the place that the Holy Ghost ought to have. That was true of the Galatians, it was true of the Corinthians. You know Paul said to them: "I cannot speak to you as to spiritual men; you ought to be spiritual men, but you are carnal." And you know how often in the course of his epistles he had to reprove and condemn them for strife and for divisions.

LACKING THE FRUIT OF THE HOLY SPIRIT

A third thought: *What are the proofs or indications that a church like the Galatians, or a*

*Christian, is serving God in the power of the flesh—is
perfecting in the flesh what was begun in the Spirit?*

The answer is very easy. Religious self-effort
always ends in sinful flesh. What was the state of
those Galatians? Striving to be justified by the works
of the law. And yet they were quarreling and in
danger of devouring one another. Count up the expressions that the apostle uses to indicate their want
of love, and you will find more than twelve—envy,
jealousy, bitterness, strife, and all sorts of expressions. Read in the fourth and fifth chapters
what he says about that. You see how they tried to
serve God in their own strength, and they failed utterly. All this religious effort resulted in failure. The
power of sin and the sinful flesh got the better of
them, and their whole condition was one of the saddest that could be thought of.

This comes to us with unspeakable solemnity.
There is a complaint everywhere in the Christian
Church of the want of a high standard of integrity
and godliness, even among the professing members
of Christian churches. I remember a sermon which I
heard preached on commercial morality. And, oh, if
we speak not only of the commercial morality or im-
morality, but if we go into the homes of Christians,
and if we think of the life to which God has called His
children, and which He enables them to live by the
Holy Ghost, and if we think of how much, nevertheless, there is of unlovingness and temper and
sharpness and bitterness, and if we think how much
there is very often of strife among the members of
churches, and how much there is of envy and
jealousy and sensitiveness and pride, then we are

compelled to say: "Where are marks of the presence of the Spirit of the Lamb of God?" Wanting, sadly wanting!

Many people speak of these things as though they were the natural result of our feebleness and cannot well be helped. Many people speak of these things as sins, yet have given up the hope of conquering them. Many people speak of these things in the church around them, and do not see the least prospect of ever having the things changed. There is no prospect until there comes a radical change, until the Church of God begins to see that every sin in the believer comes from the flesh, from a fleshly life midst our religious activities, from a striving in self-effort to serve God. Until we learn to make confession, and until we begin to see, we must somehow or other get God's Spirit in power back to His Church, we must fail. Where did the Church begin in Pentecost? There they began in the Spirit. But, alas, how the Church of the next century went off into the flesh! They thought to perfect the Church in the flesh.

Do not let us think, because the blessed Reformation restored the great doctrine of justification by faith, that the power of the Holy Spirit was then fully restored. If it is our faith that God is going to have mercy on His Church in these last ages, it will be because the doctrine and the truth about the Holy Spirit will not only be studied, but sought after with a whole heart; and not only because that truth will be sought after, but because ministers and congregations will be found bowing before God in deep abasement with one cry: "We have grieved God's Spirit; we have tried to be Christian churches

with as little as possible of God's Spirit; we have not
sought to be churches filled with the Holy Ghost."

All the feebleness in the Church is owing to the
refusal of the Church to obey its God.

And why is that so? I know your answer. You say:
"We are too feeble and too helpless, and we try to
obey, and we vow to obey, but somehow we fail."

Ah, yes; *you fail because you do not accept the
strength of God.* God alone can work out His will in
you. You cannot work out God's will, but His Holy
Spirit can; and until the Church, until believers
grasp this, and cease trying by human effort to do
God's will, and wait upon the Holy Spirit to come
with all His omnipotent and enabling power, the
Church will never be what God wants her to be, and
what God is willing to make of her.

Yielding to the Holy Spirit

I come now to my last thought, the question: *What
is the way to restoration?*

Beloved friend, the answer is simple and easy. If
that train has been shunted off, there is nothing for
it but to come back to the point at which it was led
away. The Galatians had no other way in returning
but to come back to where they had gone wrong, to
come back from all religious effort in their own
strength, and from seeking anything by their own
work, and to yield themselves humbly to the Holy
Spirit. There is no other way for us as individuals.

Is there any brother or sister whose heart is conscious: "Alas! my life knows but little of the power of
the Holy Ghost"? I come to you with God's message

that you can have no conception of what your life would be in the power of the Holy Spirit. It is too high and too blessed and too wonderful, but I bring you the message that just as truly as the everlasting Son of God came to this world and wrought His wonderful works, that just as truly as on Calvary He died and wrought out your redemption by His precious blood, so, just as truly, can the Holy Spirit come into your heart that with His divine power He may sanctify you and enable you to do God's blessed will, and fill your heart with joy and with strength. But, alas! we have forgotten, we have grieved, we have dishonored the Holy Spirit, and He has not been able to do His work. But I bring you the message: The Father in Heaven loves to fill His children with His Holy Spirit. God longs to give each one individually, separately, the power of the Holy Spirit for daily life. The command comes to us individually, unitedly. God wants us as His children to arise and place our sins before Him, and to call upon Him for mercy. Oh, are ye so foolish? Having begun in the Spirit, are ye perfecting in the flesh that which was begun in the Spirit? Let us bow in shame, and confess before God how our fleshly religion, our self-effort, and self-confidence, have been the cause of every failure.

I have often been asked by young Christians: "Why is it that I fail so? I did so solemnly vow with my whole heart, and did desire to serve God; why have I failed?"

To such I always give the one answer: "My dear friend, you are trying to do in your own strength what Christ alone can do in you."

And when they tell me: "I am sure I knew Christ

alone could do it, I was not trusting in myself," my answer always is:

"You were trusting in yourself or you could not have failed. If you had trusted Christ, He could not fail."

Oh, this perfecting in the flesh what was begun in the Spirit runs far deeper through us than we know. Let us ask God to discover to us that it is only when we are brought to utter shame and emptiness that we shall be prepared to receive the blessing that comes from on high.

And so I come with these two questions. Are you living, beloved brother-minister—I ask it of every minister of the Gospel—are you living under the power of the Holy Ghost? Are you living as an anointed, Spirit-filled man in your ministry and your life before God? O brethren, our place is an awful one. We have to show people what God will do for us, not in our words and teaching, but in our life. God help us to do it!

I ask it of every member of Christ's Church and of every believer: Are you living a life under the power of the Holy Spirit day by day, or are you attempting to live without that? Remember you cannot. Are you consecrated, given up to the Spirit to work in you and to live in you? Oh, come and confess every failure of temper, every failure of tongue however small, every failure owing to the absence of the Holy Spirit and the presence of the power of self. Are you consecrated, are you given up to the Holy Spirit?

If your answer be No, then I come with a second question—Are you *willing* to be consecrated? Are you willing to give up yourself to the power of the Holy Spirit?

You well know that the human side of consecration will not help you. I may consecrate myself a hundred times with all the intensity of my being, and that will not help me. What will help me is this—that God from Heaven accepts and seals the consecration.

And now are you willing to give yourselves up to the Holy Spirit? You can do it now. A great deal may still be dark and dim, and beyond what we understand, and you may feel nothing; but come. God alone can effect the change. God alone, who gave us the Holy Spirit, can restore the Holy Spirit in power into our life. God alone can "strengthen us with might by his Spirit in the inner man." And to every waiting heart that will make the sacrifice, and give up everything, and give time to cry and pray to God, the answer will come. The blessing is not far off. Our God delights to help us. He will enable us to perfect, not in the flesh, but in the Spirit, what was begun in the Spirit.

KEPT BY THE POWER OF GOD

THE WORDS from which I speak, you will find in I Peter 1:5. The third, fourth and fifth verses are: "Blessed be the God and Father of our Lord Jesus Christ, which . . . hath begotten us again unto a lively hope by the resurrection of Jesus Christ from the dead, to an inheritance incorruptible . . . reserved in heaven for you, who are kept by the power of God through faith unto salvation." The words of my text are: "Kept by the power of God through faith."

There we have two wonderful, blessed truths about the keeping by which a believer is kept unto salvation. One truth is, *Kept by the power of God;* and the other truth is, *Kept through faith.* We should look at the two sides—at God's side and His almighty power, offered to us to be our Keeper every moment of the day; and at the human side, we having nothing to do but in faith to let God do His keeping work. We are begotten again to an inheritance kept in Heaven for us; and we are kept here on earth by the power of God. We see there is a double keeping—*the inheritance kept for me* in Heaven, and *I on earth kept for the inheritance* there.

Now, as to the first part of this keeping, there is no doubt and no question. God keeps the inheritance in

Heaven very wonderfully and perfectly, and it is waiting there safely. And the same God keeps me for the inheritance. That is what I want to understand.

You know it is very foolish of a father to take great trouble to have an inheritance for his children, and to keep it for them, if he does not keep them for it. What would you think of a man spending his whole time and making every sacrifice to amass money, and as he gets his tens of thousands, you ask him why it is that he sacrifices himself so, and his answer is: "I want to leave my children a large inheritance, and I am keeping it for them"—if you were then to hear that that man takes no trouble to educate his children, that he allows them to run upon the street wild, and to go on in paths of sin and ignorance and folly, what would you think of him? Would not you say: "Poor man! he is keeping an inheritance for his children, but he is not keeping or preparing his children for the inheritance"! And there are so many Christians who think: "My God is keeping the inheritance for me"; but they cannot believe: "My God is keeping me for that inheritance." The same power, the same love, the same God doing the double work.

Now, I want to speak about a work God does upon us—keeping us for the inheritance. I have already said that we have two very simple truths: the one the divine side—*we are kept by the power of God;* the other, the human side—*we are kept through faith.*

KEPT BY THE POWER OF GOD

Look at the divine side: Christians are kept by the power of God.

KEEPING INCLUDES ALL

Think, first of all, that *this keeping is all-inclusive*. What is kept? *You* are kept. How much of you? The whole being. Does God keep one part of you and not another? No. Some people have an idea that this is a sort of vague, general keeping, and that God will keep them in such a way that when they die they will get to Heaven. But they do not apply that word *kept* to everything in their being and nature. And yet that is what God wants.

Here I have a watch. Suppose that this watch had been borrowed from a friend, and he said to me:

"When you go to Europe, I will let you take it with you, but mind you keep it safely and bring it back."

And suppose I damaged the watch, and had the hands broken, and the face defaced, and some of the wheels and springs spoiled, and took it back in that condition, and handed it to my friend; he would say:

"Ah, but I gave you that watch on condition that you would keep it."

"Have I not kept it? There is the watch."

"But I did not want you to keep it in that general way, so that you should bring me back only the shell of the watch, or the remains. I expected you to keep every part of it."

And so God does not want to keep us in this general way, so that at the last, somehow or other, we shall be saved as by fire, and just get into Heaven. But the keeping power and the love of God applies to every particular of our being.

There are some people who think God will keep them in spiritual things, but not in temporal things. This latter, they say, lies outside of His line. Now,

God sends you to work in the world, but He did not say: "I must now leave you to go and earn your own money, and to get your livelihood for yourself." He knows you are not able to keep yourself. But God says: "My child, there is no work you are to do, and no business in which you are engaged, and not a cent which you are to spend, but I, your Father, will take that up into my keeping." God not only cares for the spiritual, but for the temporal also. The greater part of the life of many people must be spent, sometimes eight or nine or ten hours a day, amid the temptations and distractions of business; but God will care for you there. The keeping of God includes all.

There are other people who think: "Ah! in time of trial God keeps me, but in times of prosperity I do not need His keeping; then I forget Him and let Him go." Others, again, think the very opposite. They think: "In time of prosperity, when things are smooth and quiet, I am able to cling to God, but when heavy trials come, somehow or other my will rebels, and God does not keep me then."

Now, I bring you the message that in prosperity as in adversity, in the sunshine as in the dark, your God is ready to keep you all the time.

Then again, there are others who think of this keeping thus: "God will keep me from doing very great wickedness, but there are small sins I cannot expect God to keep me from. There is the sin of temper. I cannot expect God to conquer that."

When you hear of some man who has been tempted and gone astray or fallen into drunkenness or murder, you thank God for His keeping power.

"I might have done the same as that man," you

say, "if God had not kept me." And you believe He
kept you from drunkenness and murder.

And why do you not need believe that God can
keep you from outbreaks of temper? You thought
that this was of less importance; you did not remember that the great commandment of the New Testament is—"Love one another as I have loved you."
And when your temper and hasty judgment and
sharp words came out, you sinned against the
highest law—the law of God's love. And yet you say:
"God will not, God cannot"—no, you will not say,
God cannot; but you say, "God does not keep me
from that." You perhaps say: "He can; but there is
something in me that cannot attain to it, and which
God does not take away."

I want to ask you, Can believers live a holier life
than is generally lived? Can believers experience
the keeping power of God all the day, to keep them
from sin? Can believers be kept in fellowship with
God? And I bring you a message from the Word of
God, in these words: *Kept by the power of God.*
There is no qualifying clause to them. The meaning
is, that if you will entrust yourself entirely and absolutely to the omnipotence of God, He will delight to
keep you.

Some people think that they never can get so far
as that every word of their mouth should be to the
glory of God. But it is what God wants of them, it is
what God expects of them. God is willing to set a
watch at the door of their mouth, and if God will do
that, cannot He keep their tongue and their lips? He
can; and that is what God is going to do for them that
trust Him. God's keeping is all-inclusive, and let

everyone who longs to live a holy life think out all
their needs, and all their weaknesses, and all their
shortcomings, and all their sins, and say
deliberately: "Is there any sin that my God cannot
keep me from?" And the heart will have to answer:
"No; God can keep me from every sin."

KEEPING REQUIRES POWER

Second, if you want to understand this keeping,
remember that it is not only an all-inclusive keeping, but it is an almighty keeping.

I want to get that truth burned into my soul; I want
to worship God until my whole heart is filled with the
thought of His omnipotence. God is almighty, and the
Almighty God offers Himself to work in my heart, to
do the work of keeping me; and I want to get linked
with Omnipotence, or rather, linked to the Omnipotent One, to the living God, and to have my place
in the hollow of His hand. You read the Psalms, and
you think of the wonderful thoughts in many of the
expressions that David uses; as, for instance, when
he speaks about God being *our God, our Fortress,
our Refuge, our strong Tower, our Strength* and *our
Salvation.* David had very wonderful views of how
the everlasting God is Himself the hiding place of the
believing soul, and of how He takes the believer and
keeps him in the very hollow of His hand, in the
secret of His pavilion, under the shadow of His
wings, under His very feathers. And there David
lived. And oh, we who are the children of Pentecost,
we who have known Christ and His blood and the
Holy Ghost sent down from Heaven, why is it we

know so little of what it is to walk tremblingly step by step with the Almighty God as our Keeper?

Have you ever thought that in every action of grace in your heart you have the whole omnipotence of God engaged to bless you? When I come to a man and he bestows upon me a gift of money, I get it and go away with it. He has given me something of his; the rest he keeps for himself. But that is not the way with the power of God. God can part with nothing of His own power, and therefore I can experience the power and goodness of God only so far as I am in contact and fellowship with Himself; and when I come into contact and fellowship with Himself, I come into contact and fellowship with the whole omnipotence of God, and have the omnipotence of God to help me every day.

A son has, perhaps, a very rich father, and as the former is about to commence business the father says: "You can have as much money as you want for your undertaking." All the father has is at the disposal of the son. And that is the way with God, your Almighty God. You can hardly take it in; you feel yourself such a little worm. His omnipotence needed to keep a little worm! Yes, His omnipotence is needed to keep every little worm that lives in the dust, and also to keep the universe, and therefore His omnipotence is much more needed in keeping your soul and mine from the power of sin.

Oh, if you want to grow in grace, do learn to begin here. In all your judgings and meditations and thoughts and deeds and questionings and studies and prayers, learn to be kept by your Almighty God. What is Almighty God not going to do for the child that trusts Him? The Bible says: "Above all that we can ask or think." It is Omnipotence you must learn to know and trust, and then you will live as a Christian ought to live. How little we have learned to study God, and to understand that a godly life is a life full of God, a life that loves God and waits on Him, and trusts Him, and allows Him to bless it! We cannot do the will of God except by the power of God. God gives us the first experience of His power to prepare us to long for more, and to come and claim all that He can do. God help us to trust Him every day.

KEEPING IS CONTINUOUS

Another thought. This keeping is not only all-inclusive and omnipotent, but also continuous and unbroken.

People sometimes say: "For a week or a month God has kept me very wonderfully: I have lived in the light of His countenance, and I cannot say what joy I have not had in fellowship with Him. He has blessed me in my work for others. He has given me souls, and at times I felt as if I were carried heavenward on eagle wings. But it did not continue. It was too good; it could not last." And some say: "It was necessary that I should fall to keep me humble." And others say: "I know it was my own fault; but somehow you cannot always live up in the heights."

Oh, beloved, why is it? Can there by any reason why the keeping of God should not be continuous and unbroken? Just think. All life is in unbroken continuity. If my life were stopped for half an hour I would be dead, and my life gone. Life is a continuous thing, and the life of God is the life of His Church, and the life of God is His almighty power working in us. And God comes to us as the Almighty One, and without any condition He offers to be my Keeper, and His keeping means that day by day, moment by moment, God is going to keep us.

If I were to ask you the question: "Do you think God is able to keep you one day from actual transgression?" you would answer: "I not only know He is able to do it, but I think He has done it. There have been days in which He has kept my heart in His holy presence, when, though I have always had a sinful nature within me, He has kept me from conscious, actual transgression."

Now, if He can do that for an hour or a day, why not for two days? Oh! let us make God's omnipotence as revealed in His Word the measure of our expectations. Has God not said in His Word: "I, the Lord, do keep it, and will water it every moment"? What can that mean? Does "every moment" mean every moment? Did God promise of that vineyard or red wine that *every moment* He would water it so that the heat of the sun and the scorching wind might never dry it up? Yes. In South Africa they sometimes make a graft, and above it they tie a bottle of water, so that now and then there shall be a drop to saturate what they have put about it. And so the moisture is kept there unceasingly until the graft has had time to stroke, and resist the heat of the sun.

Will our God, in His tenderhearted love toward us, not keep us every moment when He has promised to do so? Oh! if we once got hold of the thought: Our whole religious life is to be God's doing—"It is God that worketh in us to will and to do of his good pleasure"—when once we get faith to expect that from God, God will do all for us.

The keeping is to be continuous. Every morning God will meet you as you wake. It is not a question: If I forgot to wake in the morning with the thought of Him, what will come of it? If you trust your waking to God, God will meet you in the morning as you wake with His divine sunshine and love, and He will give you the consciousness that through the day you have got God to take charge of you continuously with His almighty power. And God will meet you the next day and every day; and never mind if in the practice of fellowship there comes failure sometimes. If you maintain your position and say: "Lord, I am going to expect Thee to do Thy utmost, and I am going to trust Thee day by day to keep me absolutely," your faith will grow stronger and stronger, and you will know the keeping power of God in unbrokenness.

KEPT THROUGH FAITH

And now the other side—*Believing*. "Kept by the power of God *through faith.*" How must we look at this faith?

FAITH IMPLIES HELPLESSNESS

Let me say, first of all, that this faith means utter impotence and helplessness before God.

At the bottom of all faith there is a feeling of helplessness. If I have a bit of business to transact, perhaps to buy a house, the conveyancer must do the work of getting the transfer of the property in my name, and making all the arrangements. I cannot do that work, and in trusting that agent I confess I cannot do it. And so faith always means helplessness. In many cases it means: I can do it with a great deal of trouble, but another can do it better. But in most cases it is utter helplessness; another must do it for me. And that is the secret of the spiritual life. A man must learn to say: "I give up everything; I have tried and longed, and thought and prayed, but failure has come. God has blessed me and helped me, but still, in the long run, there has been so much of sin and sadness." What a change comes when a man is thus broken down into utter helplessness and self-despair, and says: "I can do nothing!"

Remember Paul. He was living a blessed life, and he had been taken up into the third Heaven, and then the thorn in the flesh came, "a messenger of Satan to buffet me." And what happened? Paul could not understand it, and he prayed the Lord three times to take it away; but the Lord said, in effect:

"No; it is possible that you might exalt yourself, and therefore I have sent you this trial to keep you weak and humble."

And Paul then learned a lesson that he never forgot, and that was—to rejoice in his infirmities. He said that the weaker he was the better it was for him, for when he was weak, he was strong in his Lord Christ.

Do you want to enter what people call "the higher life"? Then go a step lower down. I remember Dr. Boardman telling how that once he was invited by a gentleman to go to see some works where they made fine shot, and I believe the workmen did so by pouring down molten lead from a great height. This

gentleman wanted to take Dr. Boardman up to the
top of the tower to see how the work was done. The
doctor came to the tower, he entered by the door,
and began going upstairs; but when he had gone a
few steps the gentleman called out:

"That is the wrong way. You must come down this
way; that stair is locked up."

The gentleman took him downstairs a good many
steps, and there an elevator was ready to take him to
the top; and he said:

"I have learned a lesson that going down is often
the best way to get up."

Ah, yes, God will have to bring us very low down;
there will have to come upon us a sense of emptiness
and despair and nothingness. It is when we sink
down in utter helplessness that the everlasting God
will reveal Himself in His power, and that our hearts
will learn to trust God alone.

What is it that keeps us from trusting Him perfectly?

Many a one says: "I believe what you say, but
there is one difficulty. If my trust were perfect and
always abiding, all would come right, for I know God
will honor trust. But how am I to get that trust?"

My answer is: "By the death of self. The great
hindrance to trust is self-effort. So long as you have
got your own wisdom and thoughts and strength, you
cannot fully trust God. But when God breaks you
down, when everything begins to grow dim before
your eyes, and you see that you understand nothing,
then God is coming nigh, and if you will bow down in
nothingness and wait upon God, He will become all."

As long as we are something, God cannot be all,

and His omnipotence cannot do its full work. That is the beginning of faith—utter despair of self, a ceasing from man and everything on earth, and finding our hope in God alone.

FAITH IS REST

And then, next, we must understand that faith is rest.

In the beginning of the faith-life, faith is struggling; but as long as faith is struggling, faith has not attained its strength. But when faith in its struggling gets to the end of itself, and just throws itself upon God and rests on Him, then comes joy and victory.

Perhaps I can make it plainer if I tell the story of how the Keswick Convention began. Canon Battersby was an evangelical clergyman of the Church of England for more than twenty years, a man of deep and tender godliness, but he had not the consciousness of rest and victory over sin, and often was deeply sad at the thought of stumbling and failure and sin. When he heard about the possibility of victory, he felt it was desirable, but it was as if he could not attain it. On one occasion, he heard an address on "Rest and Faith" from the story of the nobleman who came from Capernaum to Cana to ask Christ to heal his child. In the address it was shown that the nobleman believed that Christ could help him in a general way, but he came to Jesus a good deal by way of an experiment. He hoped Christ would help him, but he had not any assurance of that help. But what happened? When Christ said to him: "Go thy way, for thy child liveth," that man believed the word that Jesus spoke; he rested in that word. He had no proof that his child was well again, and he had to walk back seven hours' journey to Capernaum. He walked back, and on the way met his servant, and got the first news that the child was well, that at one o'clock on the afternoon of the previous day, at the very time that Jesus spoke to him, the fever left the child. That father rested upon the word of Jesus and His work, and he went down to Capernaum and found his child well; and he praised God, and became with his whole house a believer and disciple of Jesus.

Oh, friends, that is faith! When God comes to me with the promise of His keeping, and I have nothing on earth to trust in, I say to God: "Thy word is enough; kept by the power of God." That is faith, that is rest.

When Canon Battersby heard that address, he went home that night, and in the darkness of the night found rest. He rested on the word of Jesus. And the next morning, in the streets of Oxford, he said to a friend: "I have found it!" Then he went and told others, and asked that the Keswick Convention might be begun, and those at the convention with himself should testify simply what God had done.

It is a great thing when a man comes to rest on God's almighty power for every moment of his life, in prospect of temptations to temper and haste and anger and unlovingness and pride and sin. It is a great thing in prospect of these to enter into a covenant with the omnipotent Jehovah, not on account of anything that any man says, or of anything that my heart feels, but on the strength of the Word of God: "Kept by the power of God through faith."

Oh, let us say to God that we are going to prove Him to the very uttermost. Let us say: We ask Thee for nothing more than Thou canst give, but we want nothing less. Let us say: My God, let my life be a proof of what the omnipotent God can do. Let these be the two dispositions of our souls every day—deep helplessness, and simple, childlike rest.

That brings me to just one more thought in regard to faith—faith implies fellowship with God.

Many people want to take the Word and believe that, and they find they cannot believe it. Ah, no! you cannot separate God from His Word. No goodness or power can be received separate from God, and if you want to get into this life of godliness, you must take time for fellowship with God.

People sometimes tell me: "My life is one of such scurry and bustle that I have no time for fellowship with God." A dear missionary said to me: "People do not know how we missionaries are tempted. I get up at five o'clock in the morning, and there are the natives waiting for their orders for work. Then I have to go to the school and spend hours there; and then there is other work, and sixteen hours rush along, and I hardly get time to be alone with God."

Ah! there is the want. I pray you, remember two things. I have not told you to trust the omnipotence of God as a thing, and I have not told you to trust the Word of God as a written book, but I have told you to go to the God of omnipotence and the God of the Word. Deal with God as that nobleman dealt with the living Christ. Why was he able to believe the word that Christ spoke to him? Because in the very eyes and tones and voice of Jesus, the Son of God, he saw and heard something which made him feel that he could trust Him. And that is what Christ can do for you and me. Do not try to stir and arouse faith from within. How often I have tried to do that, and made a fool of myself! You cannot stir up faith from the depths of your heart. Leave your heart, and look into the face of Christ, and listen to what He tells you about how He will keep you. Look up into the face of your loving Father, and take time every day with Him, and begin a new life with the deep emptiness and poverty of a man who has got nothing, and who wants to get everything from Him—with the deep restfulness of a man who rests on the living God, the omnipotent Jehovah—and try God, and prove Him if He will not open the windows of Heaven and pour out a blessing that there shall not be room to receive it.

I close by asking if you are willing to experience to the very full the heavenly keeping for the heavenly inheritance? Robert Murray M'Cheyne says, somewhere: "Oh, God, make me as holy as a pardoned sinner can be made." And if that prayer is in your heart, come now, and let us enter into a covenant with the everlasting and omnipotent Jehovah afresh, and in great helplessness, but in great restfulness place ourselves in His hands. And then as we enter into our covenant, let us have the one prayer—that we may believe fully that the everlasting God is going to be our Companion, holding our hand every moment of the day; our Keeper, watching over us without a moment's in-

terval; our Father, delighting to reveal Himself in
our souls always. He has the power to let the sunshine of His love be with us all the day. Do not be
afraid because you have got your business that you
cannot have God with you always. Learn the lesson
that the natural sun shines upon you all the day, and
you enjoy its light, and wherever you are you have
got the sun; God takes care that it shines upon you.
And God will take care that His own divine light
shines upon you, and that you shall abide in that
light, if you will only trust Him for it. Let us trust God
to do that with a great and entire trust.

Here is the omnipotence of God, and here is faith
reaching out to the measure of that omnipotence.
Shall we not say: "All that that omnipotence can do,
I am going to trust my God for"? Are not the two
sides of this heavenly life wonderful? God's omnipotence covers me, and my will in its littleness
rests in that omnipotence, and rejoices in it!

> Moment by moment, I'm kept in His love;
> Moment by moment, I've life from above;
> Looking to Jesus, the glory doth shine;
> Moment by moment, Oh, Lord, I am Thine!

"YE ARE THE BRANCHES"

AN ADDRESS TO CHRISTIAN WORKERS

EVERYTHING DEPENDS on our being right ourselves in Christ. If I want good apples, I must have a good apple tree; and if I care for the health of the apple tree, the apple tree will give me good apples. And it is just so with our Christian life and work. *If our life with Christ be right,* all will come right. There may be the need of instruction and suggestion and help and training in the different departments of the work; all that has value. But in the long run, the greatest essential is to have the full life in Christ—in other words, to have Christ in us, working through us. I know how much there often is to disturb us, or to cause anxious questionings; but the Master has such a blessing for every one of us, and such perfect peace and rest, and such joy and strength, if we can only come into, and be kept in, the right attitude toward Him.

I will take my text from the parable of the Vine and the Branches, in John 15:5: "I am the vine, ye are the branches." Especially these words: "Ye are the branches."

What a simple thing it is to be a branch, the branch of a tree, or the branch of a vine! The branch grows out of the vine, or out of the tree, and there it lives and grows, and in due time, bears fruit. It has no responsibility except just to receive from the root and stem sap and nourishment. And if we only by the Holy Spirit knew our relationship to Jesus Christ, our work would be changed into the brightest and most heavenly thing upon earth. Instead of there ever being soul-weariness or exhaustion, our work would be like a new experience, linking us to Jesus as nothing else can. For, alas! is it not often true that our work comes between us and Jesus? What folly! The very work that He has to do in me, and I for Him, I take up in such a way that it separates me from Christ. Many a laborer in the vineyard has complained that he has too much work, and not time for close communion with Jesus, and that his usual work weakens his inclination for prayer, and that his too much intercourse with men darkens the spiritual life. Sad thought, that the bearing of fruit should separate the branch from the vine! That must be because we have looked upon our work as something other than the branch bearing fruit. May God deliver us from every false thought about the Christian life.

Now, just a few thoughts about this blessed branch-life.

ABSOLUTE DEPENDENCE

In the first place, it is a life of absolute dependence. The branch has nothing; it just depends upon the vine for everything. *Absolute dependence* is one of the most solemn and precious of thoughts. A great German theologian wrote two large volumes some

years ago to show that the whole of Calvin's theology
is summed up in that one principle of *absolute
dependence upon God*; and he was right. Another
great writer has said that *absolute, unalterable
dependence upon God alone* is the essence of the
religion of angels, and should be that of men also.
God is everything to the angels, and He is willing to
be everything to the Christian. If I can learn every
moment of the day to depend upon God, everything
will come right. You will get the higher life if you
depend absolutely upon God.

Now, here we find it with the vine and the branches. Every vine you ever see, or every bunch of
grapes that comes upon your table, let it remind you
that the branch is absolutely dependent on the vine.
The vine has to do the work, and the branch enjoys
the fruit of it.

What has the vine to do? It has to do a great work.
It has to send its roots out into the soil and hunt under the ground—the roots often extend a long way
out—for nourishment, and to drink in the moisture.
Put certain elements of manure in certain directions, and the vine sends its roots there, and then in
its roots or stems it turns the moisture and manure
into that special sap which is to make the fruit that is
borne. The vine does the work, and the branch has
just to receive from the vine the sap, which is
changed into grapes. I have been told that at Hampton Court, London, there is a vine that sometimes
bore a couple of thousand bunches of grapes, and
people were astonished at its large growth and rich
fruitage. Afterward it was discovered what was the
cause of it. Not so very far away runs the River
Thames, and the vine had stretched its roots away

hundreds of yards under the ground, until it had come to the riverside, and there in all the rich slime of the riverbed it had found rich nourishment, and obtained moisture, and the roots had drown the sap all that distance up and up into the vine, and as a result there was the abundant, rich harvest. The vine had the work to do, and the branches had just to depend upon the vine, and receive what it gave.

Is that literally true of my Lord Jesus? Must I understand that when I have to work, when I have to preach a sermon, or address a Bible class, or to go out and visit the poor, neglected ones, that all the responsibility of the work is on Christ?

That is exactly what Christ wants you to understand. Christ wants that in all your work, the very foundation should be the simple, blessed consciousness: Christ must care for all.

And how does He fulfill the trust of that dependence? He does it by sending down the Holy Spirit—not now and then only as a special gift, for remember the relationship between the vine and the branches is such that hourly, daily, unceasingly there is the living connection maintained. The sap does not flow for a time, and then stop, and then flow again, but from moment to moment the sap flows from the vine to the branches. And just so, my Lord Jesus wants me to take that blessed position as a worker, and morning by morning and day by day and hour by hour and step by step, in every work I have to go out to just to abide before Him in the simple utter helplessness of one who knows nothing, and is nothing, and can do nothing. Oh, beloved workers, study that word *nothing*. You sometimes sing: "Oh, to be nothing, nothing"; but have you really studied that word and prayed every day, and worshiped God, in the light of it? Do you know the blessedness of that word *nothing*?

If I am something, then God is not everything; but when I become *nothing*, God can become *all*, and the everlasting God in Christ can reveal Himself fully. That is the higher life. We need to become nothing. Someone has well said that the seraphim and cherubim are flames of fire because they know they are nothing, and they allow God to put His fullness and His glory and brightness into them. Oh, become nothing in deep reality, and, as a worker, study only one thing—to become poorer and lower and more helpless, that Christ may work all in you.

Workers, here is your first lesson: learn to be nothing, learn to be helpless. The man who has got something is not absolutely dependent; but the man who has got nothing is absolutely dependent. Absolute dependence upon God is the secret of all power in work. The branch has nothing but what it gets from the vine, and you and I can have nothing but what we get from Jesus.

DEEP RESTFULNESS

But second, the life of the branch is not only a life of entire dependence, but of deep restfulness.

That little branch, if it could think, and if it could feel, and if it could speak—that branch away in Hampton Court vine, or on some of the million vines that we have in South Africa, in our sunny land—if we could have a little branch here today to talk to us, and if we could say: "Come, branch of the vine, I want to learn from you how I can be a true branch of the living Vine," what would it answer? The little branch would whisper:

"Man, I hear that you are wise, and I know that you can do a great many wonderful things. I know you have much strength and wisdom given to you but I have one lesson for you. With all your hurry and effort in Christ's work you never prosper. The first thing you need is to come and rest in your Lord Jesus. That is what I do. Since I grew out of that vine I have spent years and years, and all I have done is just to rest in the vine. When the time of spring came I had no anxious thought or care. The vine began to pour its sap into me, and to give the bud and leaf. And when the time of summer came I had no care, and in the great heat I trusted the vine to bring moisture to keep me fresh. And in the time of harvest, when the owner came to pluck the grapes, I had no care. If there was anything in the grapes not good, the owner never blamed the branch, the blame was always on the vine. And if you would be a true branch of Christ, the living Vine, just rest on Him. Let Christ bear the responsibility."

You say: "Won't that make me slothful?"

I tell you it will not. No one who learns to rest upon the living Christ can become slothful, for the closer your contact with Christ the more of the Spirit of His zeal and love will be borne in upon you. But, oh, begin to work in the midst of your entire dependence by adding to that *deep restfulness*. A man sometimes tries and tries to be dependent upon Christ, but he worries himself about this absolute dependence; he tries and he cannot get it. But let him sink down into entire restfulness every day.

> In Thy strong hand I lay me down.
> So shall the work be done;
> For who can work so wondrously
> As the Almighty One?

Worker, take your place every day at the feet of Jesus, in the blessed peace and rest that come from the knowledge—

> I have no care, my cares are His!
> I have no fear, He cares for all my fears.

Come, children of God, and understand that it is the Lord Jesus who wants to work through you. You complain of the want of fervent love. It will come from Jesus. He will give the divine love in your heart with which you can love poeple. That is the meaning of the assurance: "The love of God is shed abroad in our hearts by the Holy Spirit"; and of that other word: "The love of Christ constraineth us." Christ can give you a fountain of love, so that you cannot help loving the most wretched and the most ungrateful, or those who have wearied you hitherto. Rest in Christ, who can give wisdom and strength, and you do not know how that restfulness will often prove to be the very best part of your message. You plead with people and you argue, and they get the idea: "There is a man arguing and striving with me." They only feel: "Here are two men dealing with each other." But if you will let the deep rest of God come over you, the rest in Christ Jesus, the peace and rest and holiness of Heaven, that restfulness will bring a blessing to the heart, even more than the words you speak.

Much Fruitfulness

But third, the branch teaches a lesson of much fruitfulness.

The Lord Jesus Christ repeated that word *fruit* often in that parable. He spoke, first, of *fruit*, and then of *more fruit*, and then of *much fruit*. Yes, you are ordained not only to bear fruit, but to bear *much fruit*. "Herein is my Father glorified, *that ye bear much fruit*." In the first place, Christ said: "I am the Vine, and my Father is the Husbandman. My Father is the Husbandman who has charge of me and you." He who will watch over the connection between Christ and the branches is God; and it is in the power of God through Christ we are to bear fruit.

Oh, Christians, you know this world is perishing for the want of workers. And it wants not only more workers—the workers are saying, some more earnestly than others: "We need not only more workers, but we need our workers to have a new power, a different life; that we workers should be able to bring more blessing." Children of God, I appeal to you. You know what trouble you take, say, in a case of sickness. You have a beloved friend apparently in danger of death, and nothing can refresh that friend so much as a few grapes, and they are out of season; but what trouble you will take to get the grapes that are to be the nourishment of this dying friend! And, oh, there are around you people who never go to church, and so many who go to church, but do not know Christ. And yet the heavenly grapes, the grapes of Eshcol, the grapes of the heavenly Vine are not to be had at any price, except as the child of God bears them out of his inner life in fellowship with Christ. Except the children of God are filled with the sap of the heavenly Vine, except they are filled with the Holy Spirit and the love of Jesus, they cannot bear much of the real heavenly grape. We all confess there is a great deal of work, a great deal of preaching and teaching and visiting, a great deal of machinery, a great deal of earnest effort of every kind; but there is not much manifestation of the power of God in it.

What is wanting? There is wanting the close connection between the worker and the heavenly Vine. Christ, the heavenly Vine, has blessings that He could pour on tens of thousands who are perishing. Christ, the heavenly Vine, has power to provide the heavenly grapes. But "Ye are the branches," and you cannot bear heavenly fruit unless you are in close connection with Jesus Christ.

Do not confound *work* and *fruit*. There may be a good deal of work for Christ that is not the fruit of the heavenly Vine. Do not seek for work only. Oh! study this question of fruit-bearing. It means the very life and the very power and the very spirit and the very love within the heart of the Son of God—it means the heavenly Vine Himself coming into your heart and mine.

You know there are different sorts of grapes, each with a different name, and every vine provides exactly that peculiar aroma and juice which gives the grape its particular flavor and taste. Just so, there is in the heart of Christ Jesus a life, and a love, and a Spirit, and a blessing, and a power for men, that are entirely heavenly and divine, and that will come down into our hearts. Stand in close connection with the heavenly Vine and say:

"Lord Jesus, nothing less than the sap that flows

through Thyself, nothing less than the Spirit of Thy divine life is what we ask. Lord Jesus, I pray Thee let Thy Spirit flow through me in all my work for Thee."

I tell you again that the sap of the heavenly Vine is nothing but the Holy Spirit. The Holy Spirit is the life of the heavenly Vine, and what you must get from Christ is nothing less than a strong inflow of the Holy Spirit. You need it exceedingly, and you want nothing more than that. Remember that. Do not expect Christ to give a bit of strength here, and a bit of blessing younder, and a bit of help over there. As the vine does its work in giving its own peculiar sap to the branch, so expect Christ to give His own Holy Spirit into your heart, and then you will bear much fruit. And if you have only begun to bear fruit, and are listening to the word of Christ in the parable, "more fruit," "much fruit," remember that in order that you should bear more fruit you just require more of Jesus in your life and heart.

We ministers of the Gospel, how we are in danger of getting into a condition of *work, work, work!* And we pray over it, but the freshness and buoyancy and joy of the heavenly life are not always present. Let us seek to understand that the life of the branch is a life of much fruit, because it is a life rooted in Christ, the living, heavenly Vine.

CLOSE COMMUNION

And fourth, the life of the branch is a life of close communion.

Let us again ask: What has the branch to do? You know that precious, inexhaustible word that Christ used: Abide. Your life is to be an abiding life. And how is the abiding to be? It is to be just like the

branch in the vine, abiding every minute of the day.
There are the branches, in close communion, in unbroken communion, with the vine, from January to
December. And cannot I live every day—it is to me
an almost terrible thing that we should ask the
question—cannot I live in abiding communion with
the heavenly Vine?

You say: "But I am so much occupied with other
things."

You may have ten hours' hard work daily, during
which your brain has to be occupied with temporal
things; God orders it so. But the abiding work is the
work of the *heart,* not of the brain, the work of the
heart clinging to and resting in Jesus, a work in
which the Holy Spirit links us to Christ Jesus. Oh, do
believe that deeper down than the brain, deep down
in the inner life, you can abide in Christ, so that
every moment you are free the consciousness will
come:

"Blessed Jesus, I am still in Thee."

If you will learn for a time to put aside other work
and to get into this abiding contract with the
heavenly Vine, you will find that fruit will come.

What is the application to our life of this abiding
communion? What does it mean?

It means *close fellowship with Christ in secret
prayer.* I am sure there are Christians who do long
for the higher life, and who sometimes have got a
great blessing, and have at times found a great inflow of heavenly joy and a great outflow of heavenly
gladness; and yet after a time it has passed away.
They have not understood that close personal actual
communion with Christ is an absolute necessity for
daily life. Take time to be alone with Christ. Nothing

in Heaven or earth can free you from the necessity
for that, if you are to be happy and holy Christians.

Oh! how many Christians look upon it as a burden
and a tax, and a duty, and a difficulty to be often
alone with God! That is the great hindrance to our
Christian life everywhere. We need more quiet
fellowship with God, and I tell you in the name of the
heavenly Vine that you cannot be healthy branches,
branches into which the heavenly sap can flow,
unless you take plenty of time for communion with
God. If you are not willing to sacrifice time to get
alone with Him, and to give Him time every day to
work in you, and to keep up the link of connection
between you and Himself, He cannot give you that
blessing of His unbroken fellowship. Jesus Christ
asks you to live in close communion with Him. Let
every heart say: "O, Christ, it is this I long for, it is
this I choose." And He will gladly give it to you.

Absolute Surrender

And then finally, the life of the branch is a life of
absolute surrender.

This word, absolute surrender, is a great and
solemn word, and I believe we do not understand its
meaning. But yet the little branch preaches it.

"Have you anything to do, little branch, besides
bearing grapes?"

"No, *nothing*."

"Are you fit for nothing?"

Fit for nothing! The Bible says that a bit of vine
cannot even be used as a pen; it is fit for nothing but
to be burned.

"And now, what do you understand, little branch,
about your relationship to the vine?"

"My relationship is just this: I am utterly given up to the vine, and the vine can give me as much or as little sap as it chooses. Here I am at its disposal and the vine can do with me what it likes."

Oh, friends, we need this absolute surrender to the Lord Jesus Christ. The more I speak, the more I feel that this is one of the most difficult points to make clear, and one of the most important and needful points to explain—what this absolute surrender is. It is often an easy thing for a man or a number of men to come out and offer themselves up to God for entire consecration, and to say: "Lord, it is my desire to give up myself entirely to Thee." That is of great value, and often brings very rich blessing. But the one question I ought to study quietly is What is meant by *absolute surrender*?

It means that, as literally as Christ was given up entirely to God, I am given up entirely to Christ. Is that too strong? Some think so. Some think that never can be; that just as entirely and absolutely as Christ gave up His life to do nothing but seek the Father's pleasure, and depend on the Father absolutely and entirely, I am to do nothing but to seek the pleasure of Christ. But that is actually true. Christ Jesus came to breathe His own Spirit into us, to make us find our very highest happiness in living entirely for God, just as He did. Oh, beloved brethren, if that is the case, then I ought to say:

"Yes, as true as it is of that little branch of the vine, so true, by God's grace, I would have it to be of me. I would live day by day that Christ may be able to do with me what He will."

Ah! here comes the terrible mistake that lies at

the bottom of so much of our own religion. A man thinks:

"I have my business and family duties, and my relationships as a citizen, and all this I cannot change. And now alongside all this I am to take in religion and the service of God, as something that will keep me from sin. God help me to perform my duties properly!"

This is not right. When Christ came, He came and bought the sinner with His blood. If there was a slave market here and I were to buy a slave, I should take that slave away to my own house from his old surroundings, and he would live at my house as my personal property, and I could order him about all the day. And if he were a faithful slave, he would live as having no will and no interests of his own, his one care being to promote the well-being and honor of his master. And in like manner I, who have been bought with the blood of Christ, have been bought to live every day with the one thought—How can I please my Master?

Oh, we find the Christian life so difficult because we seek for God's blessing while we live in our own will. We should be glad to live the Christian life according to our own liking. We make our own plans and choose our own work, and then we ask the Lord Jesus to come in and take care that sin shall not conquer us too much, and that we shall not go too far wrong; we ask Him to come in and give us so much of His blessing. But our relationship to Jesus ought to be such that we are entirely at His disposal, and every day come to Him humbly and straight-forwardly and say:

"Lord, is there anything in me that is not according to Thy will, that has not been ordered by Thee, or that is not entirely given up to Thee?"

Oh, if we would wait and wait patiently, I tell you what the result would be. There would spring up a relationship between us and Christ so close and so tender that we should afterward be amazed at how we formerly could have lived with the idea: "I am surrendered to Christ." We should feel how far distant our intercourse with Him had previously been, and that He can, and does indeed, come and take actual possession of us, and gives unbroken fellowship all the day. The branch calls us to absolute surrender.

I do not speak now so much about the giving up of sins. There are people who need that, people who have got violent tempers, bad habits, and actual sins which they from time to time commit, and which they have never given up into the very bosom of the Lamb of God. I pray you, if you are branches of the living Vine, do not keep one sin back. I know there are a great many difficulties about this question of holiness. I know that all do not think exactly the same with regard to it. That would be to me a matter of comparative indifference if I could see that all are honestly longing to be free from every sin. But I am afraid that unconsciously there are in hearts often compromises with the idea that we cannot be without sin, we must sin a little every day; we cannot help it. Oh, that people would actually cry to God: "Lord, do keep me from sin!" Give yourself utterly to Jesus, and ask Him to do His very utmost for you in keeping you from sin.

There is a great deal in our work, in our church and our surroundings that we found in the world when we were born into it, and it has grown all around us, and we think that it is all right, it cannot be changed. We do not come to the Lord Jesus and ask Him about it. Oh! I advise you, Christians, *bring everything into relationship with Jesus* and say:

"Lord, everything in my life has to be in most complete harmony with my position as a branch of Thee, the blessed Vine."

Let your surrender to Christ be absolute. I do not understand that word *surrender* fully; it gets new meanings every now and then; it enlarges immensely from time to time. But I advise you to speak it out: "Absolute surrender to Thee, O Christ, is what I have chosen." And Christ will show you what is not according to His mind, and lead you on to deeper and higher blessedness.

In conclusion, let me gather up all in one sentence. Christ Jesus said: "I am the Vine, ye are the branches." In other words: "I, the living One who have so completely given myself to you, am the Vine. You cannot trust me too much. I am the Almighty Worker, full of a divine life and power." You are the branches of the Lord Jesus Christ. If there is in your heart the consciousness that you are not a strong, healthy, fruit-bearing branch, not closely linked with Jesus, not living in Him as you should be—then listen to Him say: "I am the Vine, I will receive you, I will draw you to myself, I will bless you, I will strengthen you, I will fill you with my Spirit. I, the Vine, have taken you to be my branches, I have given myself utterly to you; children, give yourselves utterly to me. I have surrendered myself as God absolutely to you; I became man and died for you that I

might be entirely yours. Come and surrender yourselves entirely to be mine."

What shall our answer be? Oh, let it be a prayer
from the depths of our heart, that the living Christ
may take each one of us and link us close to Himself.
Let our prayer be that He, the living Vine, shall so
link each of us to Himself that we shall go away with
our hearts singing: "He is my Vine, and I am His
branch—I want nothing more—now I have the
everlasting Vine." Then, when you get alone with
Him, worship and adore Him, praise and trust Him,
love Him and wait for His love. "Thou art my Vine,
and I am Thy branch. It is enough, my soul is
satisfied."

Glory to His blessed name!

Moody Press, a ministry of the Moody Bible Institute, is
designed for education, evangelization and edification.
If we may assist you in knowing more about Christ and
the Christian life, please write us without obligation to:
Moody Press, c/o MLM, Chicago, Illinois 60610.